D1171301

OLD TESTAMENT STORIES

THE CHILD MOSES IS SAVED BY PHARAOH'S
DAUGHTER

OLD TESTAMENT STORIES

RETOLD BY

EULALIE OSGOOD GROVER

With Illustrations by
BEATRICE W. STEVENS

BOSTON
LITTLE, BROWN, AND COMPANY
1927

j 221

Copyright, 1927,
By Eulalie Osgood Grover

All rights reserved

Published September, 1927

CONTENTS

IN THE BEGINNING

	PAGE
IN THE BEGINNING	3
THE GARDEN OF EDEN	6
THE TWO BROTHERS	10
THE FIRST GIANTS	13
A YEAR IN A HOUSEBOAT	16
THE SIGN OF THE RAINBOW	19
THE TOWER OF BABEL	22
A LONG JOURNEY	26
LOT'S CHOICE	30
GOD'S WONDERFUL PROMISE	33
THE THREE GUESTS	36
LOT'S ESCAPE	40
ISAAC AND ISHMAEL	44
ABRAHAM'S GREAT TEST	47
ABRAHAM BUYS THE CAVE OF MACHPELAH	50
IN SEARCH OF A WIFE FOR ISAAC	53
REBEKAH, THE BEAUTIFUL BRIDE	56
REBEKAH'S NEW HOME	59
ESAU SELLS HIS BIRTHRIGHT	63
JACOB DECEIVES HIS FATHER	66
JACOB'S JOURNEY AND HIS DREAM	69
JACOB FINDS RACHEL	73

CONTENTS

PAGE

JACOB LEAVES HIS UNCLE 77
JACOB'S GIFTS TO ESAU AND THE WRESTLING MATCH . . 80
ESAU WELCOMES JACOB 84

THE COAT OF MANY COLORS

THE TWELVE BROTHERS 91
THE DREAMER 94
A NARROW ESCAPE 97
SOLD AS A SLAVE 100
IN AN EGYPTIAN PRISON 104
THE KING'S DREAM 107
JOSEPH BECOMES A GOVERNOR 110
THE GREAT FAMINE BEGINS 113
JOSEPH PUTS HIS BROTHERS INTO PRISON . . . 116
MYSTERIOUS MONEY 119
THE FAMINE IN CANAAN 122
A FAMILY DINNER 125
THE SILVER CUP 128
JUDAH'S PLEA AND JOSEPH'S SECRET 131
A HAPPY JOURNEY 136
THE GREAT RULER 139
THE FAMINE ENDED 143

THE BURNING BUSH

JACOB'S GRANDCHILDREN BECOME SLAVES . . . 149
HOW ONE BOY WAS SAVED 152
MOSES, THE YOUNG PRINCE 155
A NEW HOME 158
A STRANGE VOICE 161
THE WONDERFUL SIGNS 164

CONTENTS

		PAGE
THE RETURN TO EGYPT	. . . .	168
NEW BURDENS	. . . .	171
THE MAGICIANS	. . . .	174
FROGS AND MORE FROGS	. . . .	178
LICE AND FLIES	. . . .	182
THE GREAT SICKNESS	. . . .	185
A TERRIBLE HAILSTORM	. . . .	188
AN ARMY OF LOCUSTS	. . . .	191
THICK DARKNESS	. . . .	194
THE FINAL WARNING	. . . .	199
THE LAST GREAT PLAGUE	. . . .	202
THE WONDERFUL ESCAPE	. . . .	205
THE LOST EGYPTIANS	. . . .	208

THE PILLAR OF CLOUD

DAYS OF WANDERING	. . . .	215
GOD'S GIFT	. . . .	218
TROUBLE IN THE WILDERNESS	. . . .	221
THE HOLY MOUNTAIN	. . . .	225
THE GOLDEN CALF	. . . .	228
THE TEN LAWS	. . . .	232
ON THE MOVE AGAIN	. . . .	235
THE REPORT OF THE SPIES	. . . .	239
DISCOURAGEMENTS	. . . .	242
THE END OF THE JOURNEY FOR MOSES AND AARON	. .	246

THE PROMISED LAND

JOSHUA AND HIS SPIES	. . . .	253
THE ESCAPE OF THE SPIES	. . . .	256
CROSSING THE JORDAN	. . . .	259

CONTENTS

PAGE

The Fall of Jericho 262

The Defeat at Ai 266

The Victory at Ai 269

Days of Peace 272

The Battle of the Five Kings 276

The Israelites Worship Idols 279

Gideon Tears Down the Altar to Baal . . . 282

Choosing His Army 287

Gideon's Brave Band 290

The Young Samson 292

Samson's Riddle 296

Wild Ways 299

Delilah and Samson 303

The Secret of Samson's Strength 306

ILLUSTRATIONS

THE CHILD MOSES IS SAVED BY PHARAOH'S DAUGHTER *Frontispiece*

PAGE

ADAM NAMING THE ANIMALS 9

THE TOWER OF BABEL 23

THE DESTRUCTION OF SODOM 43

THE MEETING OF REBEKAH AND ELIEZER 56

JACOB'S DREAM 71

THE MEETING OF JACOB AND ESAU 85

JOSEPH IS SOLD FOR TWENTY PIECES OF SILVER . . . 101

JOSEPH INTERPRETS PHARAOH'S DREAM 110

JOSEPH MAKES HIMSELF KNOWN TO HIS BROTHERS . . 133

THE WATERS OF EGYPT ARE TURNED INTO BLOOD . . 177

MOSES BEFORE PHARAOH DURING THE PLAGUE OF DARKNESS 197

THE CROSSING OF THE RED SEA 208

MOSES STRIKES WATER FROM THE ROCK 223

MOSES BEARING THE TABLES OF STONE FROM MOUNT SINAI . 232

MOSES LOOKS UPON THE PROMISED LAND 249

JOSHUA BEFORE JERICHO 264

AN ANGEL SITTING UNDER AN OAK APPEARS TO GIDEON . 283

SAMSON SLAYS THE PHILISTINES WITH THE JAWBONE OF AN ASS 300

IN THE BEGINNING

IN THE BEGINNING

THE BIBLE opens with this beautiful story about the beginnings of all things: the heavens and the earth, the day and the night, birds, and animals, and man.

In the beginning God created the heavens and the earth, and the earth was dark and there was no life on it. The Spirit of God moved over the dark waters, and God said, "Let there be light," and light began to come.

God saw that the light was good, so he divided the light from the darkness, and he called the light Day, and the darkness he called Night.

And there was evening and there was morning, one day.

And God said, "Let there be a sky between the waters on the earth and the waters

3

above the earth." And it was so. And God called the sky the Heavens.

And there was evening and there was morning, a second day.

And God said, " Let the waters on the earth be gathered together in one place, and let the dry land appear."

And he called the dry land Earth, and the waters that he gathered together he called Seas.

God saw that this was good, and he said, " Let grass and herbs grow upon the earth, and trees bearing fruits." So grass and herbs and fruit trees, each bearing seeds of its own kind, grew upon the earth.

Again God saw that it was good. And there was evening and there was morning, a third day.

And God said, " Let there be lights in the heavens to divide the day from the night, and to mark the seasons of the year." And he made two great lights, the greater light

4

to rule the day and the lesser light to rule
the night. He made the stars also.

And there was evening and there was
morning, a fourth day.

And God said, " Let the waters swarm
with fish, and let birds fly above the earth."
And he made fish and great sea-monsters and
beautiful birds, and told them to multiply.

And there was evening and there was
morning, a fifth day.

And God said, " Let there be living crea-
tures upon the earth. Let there be cattle
and creeping things and beasts both great
and small."

When all was done, God saw that it was
a good world to look upon, and he said,
" I will now make man in my own likeness.
I will give him power over the whole earth
and over every living thing that is in it."

So God created man and woman in the
likeness of his own Spirit. And he blessed
them and said, " Be fruitful and multiply,

5

and subdue the earth, for everything in it is yours."

And there was evening and there was morning, a sixth day.

On the seventh day God rested from all his work, and he blessed the seventh day and hallowed it.

THE GARDEN OF EDEN

A DAY in God's sight is like a thousand years in man's, and it took many thousands of years for God to create the world for man to live in.

Near a broad river, beautiful shade trees began to grow, and fruit trees, and things good for food. In this lovely garden God placed man and told him he might eat the fruit of all the trees in the garden except one. This was the Tree of the Knowledge of Good and Evil. If man should eat of its fruit, God said he would surely die.

6

Into the garden God brought every animal and bird and living thing that he had made, and man gave names to them all. The man was called Adam, and his wife was named Eve.

One day when Eve was walking in the garden, a serpent said to her, " Has God said that you shall not eat the fruit of all the trees in this garden? "

" We may eat the fruit of every tree except one," Eve answered. " There is one tree the fruit of which God said we should not eat, nor even touch, lest we die."

" You shall not die," the serpent said. " God means that when you eat of the fruit of that tree, you will understand evil as well as good, as he does."

Eve saw that the Tree of the Knowledge of Good and Evil was beautiful. Its fruit looked good, and since it would make her wise, she took some and ate it and gave to her husband also.

Both Adam and Eve knew that they had

7

done wrong in choosing to know the evil as well as the good in their world. So, when they heard God's voice in the garden in the cool of the day, the man and his wife hid themselves among the trees.

But God called, saying, "Adam, where are you?"

And Adam answered, "I heard your voice in the garden and was afraid, so I hid myself."

"Have you eaten fruit from the tree that I forbade you to touch?" God asked.

"The woman gave it to me and I ate," Adam answered.

"What is this you have done?" God said to Eve.

And Eve said, "The serpent tempted me and I did eat."

Then God said to the serpent: "You shall be despised above all living things. You shall crawl upon the earth and eat dust, because you have done this thing."

8

ADAM NAMING THE ANIMALS

And he said to Eve, " Your disobedience shall bring you pain and trouble all the days of your life."

And to Adam God said, " In sweat and weariness shall you toil for your bread."

And God sent the man and the woman out of the Garden of Eden to work for their living.

THE TWO BROTHERS

ADAM and Eve left their garden home beside the river, and made a new home for themselves, but nowhere else did they find so many fruit trees and other things good for food.

The man and woman had to work hard to find enough food to eat, and they soon had two boys to feed, whom they named Cain and Abel.

After leaving the Garden of Eden, Adam and Eve were not able to talk with God in the way that they had done before. Perhaps they were afraid of him, because they had disobeyed his command. If they wished to ask for God's help and blessing, they brought a gift and burned it on a stone altar to the God whom they could not see. Cain and Abel brought gifts also.

One day, when they were grown to be young men, Cain brought to the altar some fruit that he had raised, and Abel brought a young lamb from his flock. As they offered these gifts on the altar, God showed that he was more pleased with Abel's gift than he was with Cain's. Perhaps he saw that Cain's gift was not brought in the right spirit.

When Cain saw that God liked his brother's gift better than his own, his face grew dark and angry. And God said to him : " Why are you angry? If you do what is right, your gift will be accepted. But if you do wrong, sin is waiting at your door like a wild beast ready to overcome you. You should master it."

11

But Cain did not master his sin. A few days later, when the two brothers were in the field together, Cain struck Abel a heavy blow that killed him.

As Cain ran from the field, God called to him, saying, " Where is Abel your brother? "

" I do not know," Cain answered. " Am I my brother's keeper? "

And God said : " What have you done? Your brother's blood cries to me from the ground. Never again shall the ground yield fruit for your labor. You shall be a wanderer upon the earth."

" My punishment is greater than I can bear! " Cain cried. " If I am driven from this land, God will be hidden from me, and whoever finds me will kill me."

But God said : " Whoever kills Cain shall be punished sevenfold." And he placed a mark upon him, so that no one might kill him.

Cain then left his home, never to return.

12

He and his wife went to the east and lived in the land of Nod. There they had a son whom they named Enoch. And they built a city which they called Enoch, after their son.

Many years went by, and Enoch's great-great-grandson, Lamech, became the father of three boys. They were Jabal, Jubal, and Tubal-Cain.

It is said that Jabal became the father of those who lived in tents and owned cattle, while Jubal invented the harp and the organ-pipe. And Tubal-Cain made the first sharp instruments from brass and iron.

THE FIRST GIANTS

Abel was killed and Cain had gone into another country to live. But Adam and Eve were not left alone, for they had other children, and they began to have grand-children and great-grandchildren.

13

Because Adam and Eve disobeyed God in the garden, their children grew up to be disobedient, too, living selfish, wicked lives.

These people not only lived to be very old, but they grew to be very large. They were giants in size. One man, whose name was Methuselah, lived nearly a thousand years. He was nine hundred and sixty-nine years old when he died. He was probably the oldest man who has lived since the world began.

Methuselah had a grandson called Noah, who lived almost as many years as his grandfather. When Noah was about five hundred years old, he had three boys whom he named Shem, Ham, and Japheth.

Noah was a good man who tried to obey God's laws, and his sons grew up to be good men like him. But the other men of that time were very wicked.

When God saw how wicked the people were, he was sorry that he had ever made

14

men to live upon the earth. And he said: "I must destroy them all. I will save only Noah and his family, for they are the only good people living."

And God said to Noah: "These people shall live a hundred and twenty years longer. If they have not forgotten their wicked ways then, I will destroy them. I will send a great flood. It shall rain forty days and forty nights. The whole earth shall be covered with water. Everything living shall be drowned. But you and your family shall be saved, because you are trying to do right."

God then told Noah to build a large houseboat, or Ark — long and wide and deep. It should be three stories high, with rooms in it and a roof over all. There must be a door also, and a long, narrow window just under the roof to let in light and air. It was to be built so that it could float upon the water, and be covered with pitch inside and out to prevent leaking.

God said that when the Ark was finished Noah should go into it with his wife and his three sons and their wives. He told him, also, to take into the Ark two of every kind of animal and creeping thing and bird that lived upon the earth, and seven of every animal and fowl that was good for food or for sacrifice. So when the great flood should come, not all of the animals would be drowned.

A YEAR IN A HOUSEBOAT

It was a long, hard task to build the Ark, even for such big men as Noah and his three sons. They worked many years upon it. Nothing like it had ever been built. It was as large as a great ship — nearly five hundred feet long, eighty feet high, and fifty feet wide.

The other people all laughed at the four men for building such a great boat on dry land, for the nearest water on which to sail it was a thousand miles away. But Noah remembered what God had said to him, and he was going to be ready.

And Noah was ready. At the end of a hundred and twenty years, God spoke to him again. He told him to take his family and all of the animals quickly into the Ark, for in seven days a great rain would begin.

So Noah and his sons led the animals into the Ark two by two. There were big animals and little animals. There were elephants and sheep and cattle and doves and snakes — everything that lived upon the earth or in the air. But the fish that lived in the water were not taken in.

God then told Noah and his family to take food into the Ark, enough to last them a whole year. No one helped them with the work, for no one else believed that anything unusual was going to happen.

In those days people thought that the sky

17

was a solid dome arching over the flat earth.
They thought that above the dome, and below the earth, there was nothing but water.
When it rained, they believed that windows
were opened in the sky to let the water pour
down, and that even the deep waters below
the earth sometimes burst through and
flooded the land.

The floods had never lasted long, so the
people laughed at Noah and his family for
shutting themselves into their Ark on dry
land. But while they laughed, the windows
of heaven suddenly opened, and it rained as
it had never rained before.

For forty days and forty nights it rained.
The rivers soon overflowed. People ran to
the hills for safety. When the hills were
covered with water, they ran to the tops of
the mountains.

At last there was not a spot of dry land
left anywhere, and every living thing upon
the earth was drowned. But Noah's great

Ark floated safely about upon the deep water.

When the eight people who lived in the Ark looked out of their high window, they could see only water and sky everywhere.

For many months the Ark drifted about, but at last God sent a great wind to help carry the water away. Day after day the wind blew, and day after day the water grew less and less.

THE SIGN OF THE RAINBOW

ONE day there was great excitement in the Ark. It was standing still! The people who lived in it could feel that they were not drifting about on the water any longer. In floating over a high mountain the Ark had touched ground and rested there. It was on the top of Mount Ararat.

Noah and his family were eager to know if the trees and the grass had begun to

19

grow again, so they opened their window and let a raven and a dove fly out. The dove soon flew back to them, and Noah knew that water still covered the land. But the raven was stronger and flew about until dry land appeared, for the water was fast going away.

After waiting another week, Noah let the dove fly away again. This time it brought back in its bill a green leaf picked from an olive tree. The olive leaf showed that the water had gone down and that the trees were beginning to grow again.

After still another week, the dove was sent out a third time, and this time it did not return. Noah and his sons then quickly took off the roof of the Ark, and they saw dry land all about them.

God now spoke to Noah again, saying: "Come out of the Ark, and bring your wife and your sons and your sons' wives with you. Bring all the animals and the

20

birds and the creeping things with you, that there may be life upon the earth once more.''

So the door of the Ark was opened, and they all went out upon dry land. They had lived in the Ark for more than a year, and they thanked God for saving their lives in so wonderful a way. The first thing that Noah did was to build an altar, and offer sacrifice to God, promising that he and his family would try to do God's will.

God was pleased with Noah's offering, and he said to him: '' Never again will I destroy the earth by a flood. Day and night, spring and summer, fall and winter shall come without change. The earth is yours. You shall be the rulers of the ground, and of every living thing upon it. The rainbow which I have set in the sky shall be a sign of my promise to you and to all people after you.''

So God blessed Noah and his sons, and they became farmers and planted vineyards.

21

Noah was about six hundred years old at this time, but he lived to be nine hundred and fifty years old — almost as old as his grandfather, Methuselah.

THE TOWER OF BABEL

AFTER the flood, Noah and his three sons and their families continued to live near the two great rivers now called the Euphrates and the Tigris. They had large families, and they moved about more than the people did before the flood. They needed more room for their vineyards, and more pasture land for their cattle and sheep.

In their wanderings some of the people came to a broad, fertile plain between the two rivers. They found that the clay soil there could be made into bricks, which baked hard under the hot sun.

They said to each other: "Come, let us make bricks and build us a city. Let us

THE TOWER OF BABEL

build a high tower whose top shall reach unto heaven, and shall be seen from afar. We shall make a name for ourselves and become a great people, and shall not be scattered over the face of the whole earth."

So they set to work making bricks, drying them in the hot sun. They built a great foundation for their tower, using soft clay to hold the bricks together. They worked hard, carrying clay and bricks, and climbing higher and higher as the tower rose. They laughed and shouted and talked together, for they were proud of what they were doing.

Finally, God saw the pride in the hearts of the children of men over the city they were building and the great tower that would soon reach unto heaven.

And God said: " These people think the same thoughts and speak the same language. If they continue to live together in the same place, they will soon have everything that they want and will forget their God. The wicked will lead the good astray, and they will become as wicked as their fathers were before the flood. I will make them speak different languages, so that they cannot understand each other. They will then scatter over the earth, and some will surely remember my ·laws and obey them."

So, little by little, the people began to talk in different ways. After a time, those in one family could not understand what the people of another family were saying. And as the men who were working on the great tower could no longer talk together, they stopped their work, and the tower was never finished.

The city was named Babel, which means " confusion "; for it was there that the great confusion of languages began. Later it was called Babylon, and for a long time it was one of the greatest cities in that part of the world.

Because of the different languages, many people left Babel, those who spoke the same language going together. Some went north and built the city of Nineveh, in a land called Assyria. Others went to the west, as far as the great river Nile, and founded the land of Egypt. And still others went to the shore of the Great Sea and built the cities of Tyre and Sidon.

And once more the world had many people in it, but they now lived in many lands and spoke many languages.

A LONG JOURNEY

About two hundred miles southeast of Babylon, the two great rivers, Tigris and Euphrates, flow together just before reaching the sea. Here a group of people settled and called their land Chaldea. And they built a city which they named Ur.

The people of Chaldea did not know God,

but worshiped idols of the sun and the moon, made of wood and stone.

After a time, a man named Terah lived in Ur, who had three sons named Abram, Nahor, and Haran. Terah and his sons tried to live better lives than did the people around them, for they knew a little about the God who had saved Noah and his family from the great flood.

At last, Abram and his father decided to leave Ur. Abram's brother Haran had died, but Haran's son Lot went with them, as did also Abram's wife Sarai. But Nahor stayed behind in the land of his birth.

The three men took their tents, their cattle, their flocks of sheep, and their many servants, and followed up the river Euphrates for more than five hundred miles, until they came to the city of Haran near the mountains.

Terah was growing old, and perhaps the wandering life was too hard for him, for they all stayed in Haran until Terah died at the age of two hundred and five years.

Abram was seventy-five years old at this time, and God spoke to him, saying: "Get you up and leave your country and your father's house and all your kinsmen, and go to the land that I shall show you. I will make a great nation of your family. I will bless you and will make your name famous."

So Abram set out as God commanded him. He took Sarai his wife, and Lot his brother's son, and everything that they had. They journeyed southwest toward the land of Canaan by the Great Sea. On one side were the mountains, and on the other side was the great desert.

Finally they reached the land of Canaan and came to the place of Shechem, where there was a large oak tree. As they rested under the oak, God said to Abram again, "To your children will I give all this land."

And Abram built an altar to God, and worshiped him there. Then they went on a little farther and set up their tents on a mountain between Bethel and Ai, where Abram built another altar. And so they journeyed slowly southward.

After a time a famine came upon the land, for the summers in Canaan were hot and dry, and there was but little rain. So Abram and Lot took their cattle and sheep down to the green pastures of Egypt, near the river Nile. They stayed in Egypt for some time, for the famine was great in Canaan. But at last they returned to Bethel where they had built the altar to God, and there they were glad to worship him again, for in Egypt the people worshiped only idols.

LOT'S CHOICE

W<small>HILE</small> they were in Egypt, Abram and Lot gained many sheep and cattle and camels and donkeys. They were rich men, not only in cattle, but in silver and gold and tents and servants.

The two men soon found, however, that the land near Bethel was not fertile enough to feed so many herds and flocks. Their shepherds began to quarrel, each wanting the best pastures for his own cattle and sheep. Then, too, many Canaanites lived in that part of the land, and there was not enough room for them all.

So Abram said to Lot: "Let there be no quarrel between you and me, nor between your men and my men, for we are like brothers. The whole land is open to us. Let us separate. If you choose to go to the left, I will go to the right, or if you choose the right, then I will go to the left."

Lot looked about him and saw that the valley of the Jordan River was well watered and the grass was green, so he chose that part of the land. It was like a great garden, with the cities of Sodom and Gomorrah lying in the midst of it.

So Lot took his servants and all his possessions and went down to the plain to live, pitching his tents near the city of Sodom. But he did not know that the people of Sodom were the most wicked people in all the land.

After Lot had made his choice, God spoke to Abram, saying: " Lift up your eyes and look from the place where you are standing — north and south and east and west. As far as your eye can see, the land shall belong to you and to your children and to your children's children forever. They shall be as the dust of the earth in number. Arise and walk through the length and breadth of the land, for it is yours."

Abram then moved his tents from Bethel, and went south as far as Hebron, and lived near the oaks of Mamre. And he built an altar there to Jehovah.

After a time, there was a great battle fought on the plain near Sodom. The kings of Sodom and Gomorrah were beaten and their soldiers killed.

The king who won the battle took whatever he wanted from the city of Sodom, and carried the people away to be his slaves. Lot and his family and all his possessions were carried away, too. They were taken far to the north near the headwaters of the river Jordan.

But there was a man in the battle who ran away and brought the news of Lot's capture to his uncle Abram, who was still living near Hebron.

Abram quickly gathered together all the men who were with him and followed the army, coming upon them suddenly in the night while the soldiers were asleep. Abram fought them fiercely and they ran for the mountains, leaving everything behind them. He then took Lot and his family, and all the people of Sodom with their goods, and brought them back to their homes. It was a great victory.

GOD'S WONDERFUL PROMISE

THE king of Sodom was grateful to Abram for saving his people, and wanted to make him a present of all the things that they had brought back. "Give me the people," the king said, "and you shall have the goods."

But Abram said: "I have made a promise to God that I will take nothing, not even a thread or a shoelace that belongs to you, lest you should say you have made Abram rich."

So Abram went back to his tents under

33

the oak trees near Hebron, while Lot and his family stayed in the city of Sodom with those who worshiped idols.

Soon God spoke to Abram, saying, " Fear not, Abram, I will protect you and will reward you greatly."

But Abram said : " O Lord Jehovah, what will you do for me? I have no child, and all my possessions will be given, when I die, to Eliezer, who is the steward of my house."

Although Abram had a large family of people around him, and many servants, he and Sarai had no son of their own, and they were both growing old. But God spoke to Abram again, and said : " Your property shall not be given to a servant, but to your own son. Look up at the heavens and try to count the stars. Even so great shall the number of your children's children be in the years to come."

And Abram believed, and trusted God's promise.

Then God said: "After your death your people shall go into a strange land, where they shall become slaves and be cruelly treated. But many years later they shall leave the land, not as slaves, but rich with much goods. They shall return to this land that is now your home and it shall be their land again."

So God made a covenant with Abram, and promised to give him a son and a people and a land. And Abram promised to serve God faithfully.

And God said: "Your name shall no longer be Abram, but Abraham, which means 'Father of many people.' And your wife's name shall be changed from Sarai to Sarah. I will bless her and give her a son, and his name shall be called Isaac. She shall be the mother of kings and of many nations."

Not long after this, as Abraham was sitting in the door of his tent during the heat of the day, he saw three men coming toward him. Abraham knew that they were not common men, and he ran to meet them, bowing with his face to the ground.

"My Lord," he said, "I beg you not to pass me by. Water shall be brought to wash your feet. You shall rest in the shade of these trees and have food to strengthen you, and you shall then pass on your way."

"Do as you have said," the strangers answered him. And they came under his trees and rested there.

THE THREE GUESTS

AFTER the arrival of the three strangers, Abraham hurried into the tent and said to Sarah, "Take three measures of fine meal, and knead it, and make it into cakes." He then ran to his herd and brought a calf, and gave it to a servant who prepared it for cooking.

When all was ready, Abraham took the

cakes and the meat, with butter and milk, and set the food before his guests under the trees. Then he stood by and watched them eat.

When they had finished eating, the one whom Abraham called " my Lord " told Abraham that he and Sarah would soon have a son. He said that the boy should be called Isaac, which means " laughing," because both Abraham and Sarah laughed aloud when they heard the good news.

The three strangers then rose to go on their way, and Abraham went a part of the way with them.

And Jehovah the Lord said : " I will tell thee, Abraham, what I am about to do. The people of Sodom and Gomorrah have sinned greatly. I am going down to see how great their sin is."

Abraham knew that the people on the plain were very wicked. He feared that God would destroy them all, even Lot and his

37

family. So he said: "O Lord, will you destroy the good with the wicked? If there should be fifty good people in the city of Sodom, will you not spare the city for their sakes? You are too just to kill the good with the wicked."

And the Lord answered, "If there should be fifty good people in the city of Sodom, I will not destroy it."

Then Abraham said: "I know that I should not ask for more, for I am but a common man talking with the Lord God. But if there should lack five people to make up the fifty, will you destroy the city for lack of the five?"

"If I find forty and five good people in the city, I will not destroy it," was the answer.

"But what if there should be only forty good people?" Abraham asked.

"I will save the city for the sake of the forty."

Then Abraham said: "Oh, let not the Lord be angry with me, and I will speak yet once more. Perhaps there may be only thirty good people in Sodom."

And the Lord said, "I will not destroy the city if I find thirty there."

"But if there should be only twenty, what will you do then?"

"I will not destroy it, for the twenty's sake."

"Let me speak but this once, O Lord," Abraham said. "Perhaps there may be no more than ten good people in the city?"

"I will not destroy the city, for the sake of the ten," was the answer.

LOT'S ESCAPE

EARLY in the evening, two strangers appeared in Sodom and found Lot, sitting by the city gate. When Lot saw them, he rose, and bowed with his face to the earth, and said: "I beg you, sirs, to spend the night in my house. Your feet shall be washed, and you shall rise up early in the morning and go on your way."

"No, we must spend the night in the street," the strangers answered him. But Lot urged them strongly, and they went with him to his house, where he made a feast.

The people of the city heard that there were strangers in Lot's house, and before the men had lain down for the night, the house was surrounded by a noisy crowd, both young and old from all parts of the town.

"Where are the men who came here to-night?" the people shouted. "Bring them out, that we may see them."

Lot knew that the people meant to harm the men, so he went out and closed the door behind him. "I beg you, my friends," he said, "not to harm these men who have come under my roof."

But they only answered him: "Stand back, or we shall treat you worse than we do them. Are you a judge over us?"

The people then pushed hard against Lot, and were about to break down the door when the strange men drew Lot into the house, and smote all the people with blindness, so that they soon grew tired trying to find the door.

The strangers then said to Lot: "Are there others in your family, any sons, or sons-in-law, or daughters? If so, bring them out of the city quickly, for we have come to destroy it because of its wickedness."

So Lot went out and said to his sons-in-law: "Up, get you out of this place, for Jehovah is going to destroy the city." But his sons-in-law thought he was only jesting, and they laughed at him.

Early the next morning, the two strangers urged Lot to make haste, saying, " Arise, take your wife and your two daughters and go away, lest you all be destroyed with the wicked in the city."

But Lot was slow in starting, so the men took him and his wife and his daughters by the hand, and led them out of the city, and the Lord said : " Run for your lives. Do not look behind you, nor stop on the plain. Flee to the mountains, that you may not be destroyed."

" Oh, not so far, Lord!" cried Lot. " Harm will surely come to us before we can reach the mountains. Let us run to that little city on the plain, and be safe."

And the Lord said : " Do as you wish. I will not destroy the city to which you go. Make haste now, for I can do nothing until you are there."

THE DESTRUCTION OF SODOM

ISAAC AND ISHMAEL

Lot and his family reached the little city of Zoar just as the morning sun was rising. In crossing the plain, Lot's wife had wanted to see what was happening behind her, and against the Lord's command, she looked back; and she was changed to a pillar of salt, and left standing there on the plain.

A rain of fire then fell upon Sodom and Gomorrah. The two cities, with all the people in them, and everything that grew upon the ground, were completely destroyed.

When Abraham looked down over the plain toward Sodom and Gomorrah, he saw smoke rising as if from a great furnace, and he supposed that Lot and all his family were dead.

Soon after this, Abraham moved his tents to Gerar, not far from the Great Sea, and there a son was born to him and to Sarah, as God had promised. Abraham was a

44

hundred years old when the child was born, and they named the boy Isaac.

A beautiful slave girl named Hagar was living in Abraham's family. She, too, had a young son whose father was Abraham. The boy's name was Ishmael.

Ishmael and Isaac played much together, for they were half brothers. But Ishmael was the older and he sometimes teased his younger brother.

Sarah was jealous of Ishmael, and said to Abraham: "Send this slave girl and her boy away. He shall not be an heir in your family with my son Isaac."

This grieved Abraham, for he loved both of his sons. But God said to him: "Be not sad. Do as Sarah has asked, for only Isaac and his children shall bear your name. But I will make a nation from Ishmael also, for he is your son."

So the next morning Abraham sent Hagar and her boy away. He gave them bread and a goatskin bottle filled with water, which Hagar carried upon her shoulder.

Hagar started to go back to her home in Egypt, but she had not gone far when she became lost in the desert of Beersheba. She wandered about until her water and food were gone. Then she laid her tired child in the shade of a desert shrub, and sat down a little distance away, crying, " I cannot see the child die." And she wept bitterly.

But God heard the cries of Hagar and her child, and said : " What troubles you, Hagar? Fear not. Arise and lift up your boy, for I will make of him a great nation."

Hagar then saw a well of water that she had not seen before. So she filled her bottle and gave Ishmael to drink, and he did not die.

Hagar and Ishmael lived many years in the desert, and Ishmael became a famous bowman. His mother found a wife for him

46

in Egypt, and his people became the Arabs of the desert.

ABRAHAM'S GREAT TEST

It was hard for Abraham to send Hagar and Ishmael away, but he was soon asked to do something much harder.

One day God said to him, " Abraham." And Abraham answered, " Here am I." Then God said : " Take your son, your only son Isaac whom you love, and go to the land of Moriah. On a mountain there, which I shall show you, you shall offer your son as a burnt offering."

Abraham's heart was sad indeed. He and Sarah were both old. Isaac was their only child. God had promised that many people should come from Abraham's family, but how could this be if his only son was killed?

In those days people often gave the lives

of their dearest ones to show their great love and loyalty. So, since God had asked it, Abraham was ready to sacrifice even his son.

The next morning Abraham rose early and saddled his donkey and split wood for the burnt offering. He then took Isaac and two of his young menservants, and started toward the land of Moriah.

They had traveled three days when Abraham saw in the distance the place to which he was going. He said to the young men: " Stay here with the donkey, while the lad and I go on to worship. We will then come back to you."

So Abraham took the wood for the burnt offering from the donkey, and gave it to Isaac to carry. The fire and the knife he carried himself, and they went on together.

After walking some distance in silence, Isaac said, " My father! We have the fire and the wood, but where is the lamb for the burnt offering? "

" God will provide the lamb, my son,"
Abraham answered, for he could not yet
tell the lad what he was about to do.

When they came to the place of which
God had spoken, Abraham built an altar
and laid the wood upon it. He then bound
Isaac his son, and laid him on the wood
upon the altar.

But as Abraham raised his knife, an angel
of God called, " Abraham, Abraham!"
And he answered, " Here am I."

And the angel said, " Do not put your
hand upon the boy, nor harm him, for I
know how great is your love for God, since
you have not withheld your only son."

Abraham then looked up and saw a ram
caught by the horns in the bush near by.
He took the ram and offered him as a burnt
offering, instead of his own son. And he
called the place by a name which means,
" God will provide."

Then the angel spoke to Abraham a second

time, declaring : "The Lord says, 'Because you have not withheld your son, your only son, I will bless you, and will make your children as the stars of the heavens, and as the sand upon the seashore in number. They shall conquer their enemies, and all nations shall be blessed because you have obeyed my voice.'"

ABRAHAM BUYS THE CAVE OF MACHPELAH

THE three days' journey from Mount Moriah back to their home in Beersheba, near the desert, was a happy one for Abraham and Isaac. Isaac felt that he now belonged to God. And Abraham had learned that God did not wish the lives of children or men sacrificed in worship to him.

As years went by, the people about them continued to offer human sacrifices to their idols, but Abraham and his descendants

50

offered only oxen and sheep and goats to their God.

After a time, Sarah, the wife of Abraham and the mother of Isaac, died at the age of a hundred and twenty-seven years. Though Abraham had lived in the land of Canaan many years, he did not own a family burial-place. So he went to the sons of Heth, in Hebron, and said, " I beg you to sell me a piece of ground where I may bury my dead."

The sons of Heth answered him: " Thou art a prince of God among us. In the choice of our sepulchres bury thy dead."

Abraham then bowed himself before the people and asked to be allowed to buy the cave of Machpelah.

Ephron, the owner of the cave, said, " Not so, my lord. Hear me! The cave, and the field that is around it, I give to thee before all these people."

But Abraham again bowed himself before them, and said : " I will gladly pay the full price of the field. Take it from me, and let me bury my dead."

"Listen to me, my lord," Ephron answered. "A piece of ground worth four hundred shekels of silver — what is that between me and thee? Bury thy dead."

Abraham understood the courtesy of the people of the land, and he weighed out four hundred shekels of silver and gave it to Ephron.

So the field, and the cave of Machpelah with all the trees growing around it, became the property of Abraham and his family for many generations. Here Sarah was buried, and later, Abraham and their son Isaac. And here, too, many years later, the body of Jacob was brought by a great procession of people from the distant land of Egypt, and laid to rest with much pomp.

And again, when the Hebrew people returned to the Promised Land after their long years of exile, the cave was opened to receive the body of Joseph, who had saved his people during the great famine.

So the cave of Machpelah, which Abraham bought for four hundred shekels of silver, became the tomb of the greatest leaders of Israel.

IN SEARCH OF A WIFE FOR ISAAC

AFTER the death of Sarah, Abraham felt that it was time for his son Isaac to marry. It was the custom in those days for parents to choose wives or husbands for their sons and daughters.

Abraham did not wish Isaac to marry a woman from the land in which they were living, for these women were worshipers of idols. So he called Eliezer, his head servant, and said: " My son must not marry a daughter of the Canaanites among whom we dwell. You shall go to my kinsmen, in my own country, and there find a wife for Isaac."

"But what if the woman whom I shall choose should not be willing to follow me back to this strange land?" Eliezer asked. "Shall I then take your son back to the land from which you came?"

And Abraham answered: "Isaac shall not return to my native land. Jehovah, the God who took me from my father's house, brought me into this land and promised to give it to my children and to my children's children. God will send an angel before you, and you shall find a wife for my son. If she will not return with you, you shall be released from your promise."

So Eliezer promised Abraham that he would find a wife for Isaac in his native land, and he made ready for the long journey. Ten camels were loaded with rich gifts for the bride and her family.

Eliezer traveled back over the same road, between the mountains and the desert, that Abram and Sarai and Lot had taken nearly

THE MEETING OF REBEKAH AND ELIEZER

And Rebekah answered him: "I am the daughter of Bethuel, the son of Nahor. There is room in my father's house for you, and food for your camels also."

Eliezer bowed his head and thanked God for answering his prayer and for bringing him to his master's own family. He then told Rebekah that he was the servant of Abraham, the brother of her grandfather Nahor. And Rebekah ran home to tell her parents of the stranger she had met at the well, and to show the presents that he had given her.

When Rebekah's brother Laban saw the ring and the golden bracelets, and heard the words that the stranger had said to his sister, he ran to the well to meet the man.

As Laban came near, he saw Eliezer standing by the well with his camels, and he said: "Come in, O favored one of God. Why do you stand outside the gate? Our house is ready for you, and there is room for your camels as well."

So Eliezer went home with Laban and unloaded his camels. His sandals were removed, and water was brought to wash his feet and the feet of the men who were with him, as was the custom of the land, and food was set before them.

But Eliezer said, " I cannot eat until I have told you my errand. I am Abraham's servant. God has greatly blessed my master. He has flocks and herds and silver and gold and menservants and maidservants and camels and asses. A son was born to Abraham and his wife, when they were both old, and to him Abraham has given all his possessions.

" I have promised my master that I would not take a wife for his son from the daughters of the Canaanites among whom he lives, but that I would come back to his father's house and to his own kindred, and here find a wife for Isaac. God has sent an angel before me and has brought me to your daughter Rebekah. Tell me, will you deal kindly with Abraham my master? "

Bethuel and Laban then said: "This is God's will. See, Rebekah is here. Take her, and she shall be the wife of your master's son."

When Eliezer heard these words, he bowed his head to the ground in thanksgiving. He then gave Rebekah the gifts that he had brought, jewels of silver and of gold, and rich garments to wear. There were gifts also for Rebekah's mother, and for Laban her brother.

A great feast was then made for Eliezer and his men, who spent the night in Bethuel's home.

REBEKAH'S NEW HOME

The next morning, Eliezer said to Bethuel: "I must return to my master. Send me on my way with your daughter."

"Oh, not so soon!" cried the mother and brother of Rebekah. "Let the maiden stay with us a few days longer — ten days at least. Then she shall go with you."

But Eliezer answered: "Do not delay me. God has given me what I came for, and I must go back to my master."

"We will let the maiden answer for herself," said the father. And he called Rebekah to him, and said, "Wilt thou go?"

And Rebekah said, "I will go."

So the family gave her their blessing, and Rebekah, with her nurse and her maids, started with Abraham's servant toward her new home. The women rode upon camels, following behind Eliezer.

The journey was long, but at last the travelers reached Canaan, and came near the place where Abraham and Isaac lived. It was early evening, and as Isaac walked in the field, he looked up and saw his own camels approaching.

When Rebekah saw Isaac, she got down from her camel and said to the servant, " Who is this man coming through the field to meet us? "

" He is the son of my master," Eliezer answered.

Rebekah knew that this was the man who was to be her husband, so she covered herself with her veil, as was the custom for a bride to do when she met the man whom she was to marry.

Eliezer then told Isaac all the things that he had done. And Isaac brought Rebekah to his mother's tent, and she became his wife, and he loved her and was comforted after his mother's death.

Some years later, Abraham died at the age of a hundred and seventy-five years. His two sons, Isaac and Ishmael, buried their father beside his wife Sarah in the Cave of Machpelah, which Abraham had bought from Ephron.

Then Isaac became the owner of all the riches of his father Abraham, his tents and servants and flocks of sheep and herds of cattle and camels.

Isaac was a quiet, peaceful man and did not move his tents so often as his father had done, but lived many years in one place; and twin sons were born to his wife Rebekah. The boys were named Esau and Jacob. As the two brothers grew up, Esau became a skillful hunter with his bow and arrow, and he liked to wander alone in the woods. But Jacob was a thoughtful boy who stayed at home and helped his mother with the work about the tents. Esau's skin was rough and hairy, while Jacob's was smooth and fine.

Rebekah loved Jacob a little better than she did Esau, but her husband loved Esau the better, for Esau often brought venison home from the hunt for his father to eat.

ESAU SELLS HIS BIRTHRIGHT

IN Isaac's day, the oldest son received the largest share of his father's property, and was given a special blessing at the father's death. This was called the older son's birthright.

Although Esau and Jacob were twins, Esau had come first, so the family birthright would go to him. But Esau did not seem to care for the birthright, though the more thoughtful brother often wished that it might be his own.

One day, when Jacob was making a stew of lentils and bread, his brother came home hungry and tired from a long hunt.

" Give me some of that red pottage! " he cried, as he came near the tents. " I am ready to faint."

" Let me have your birthright and you shall have the pottage," Jacob answered, for he saw his chance to get what he wanted.

63

"I am dying with hunger. Of what use is the birthright to me? Take it." Esau answered.

So Esau sold his birthright to his brother for a bowl of lentils and bread, and he sat down upon the ground and ate and drank.

The years went by, and at last Isaac knew that he was growing old and might soon die. His strength was gone, and he was almost blind. So he called Esau, his elder son, to him and said, "My son!"

And Esau answered, "Here am I."

And Isaac said: "I am old. I do not know when I may die. Take your bow and your quiver of arrows, and go out and shoot a deer. Make a savory dish of venison, such as I love, and bring it to me that I may eat and bless you before I die."

So Esau took his bow and arrows and went to the fields to hunt for a deer.

Now Rebekah heard all that Isaac had said to his son. She did not want the father's blessing to go to Esau, but to her favorite son Jacob. So she said to Jacob: "Listen to me. Your father has sent your brother out to kill a deer. Esau will make a savory dish of venison for him to eat, and your father will bless Esau before he dies.

"My son, do as I tell you. Go to your flock of goats and bring me two kids. I will make savory food of them, such as your father loves, and you shall take it to him and shall receive his blessing instead of Esau."

But Jacob said to his mother: "My brother Esau has hairy skin, while my skin is smooth. My father will feel my arms and will know that I am deceiving him. He will then give me a curse instead of a blessing."

"The curse shall be upon me, my son," said Jacob's mother. "Only obey my command and fetch me the kids."

JACOB DECEIVES HIS FATHER

So Jacob brought two kids to his mother, and she prepared food such as his father loved. She then put Esau's best clothes upon Jacob, and covered his hands and his neck with the skin of the kids.

And Jacob took the food and went to his father's tent, and said, "My father!"

And his father answered, "Here am I. Which one are you, my son?"

"I am Esau, your first-born," Jacob answered. "I have done what you asked. I beg you to eat of my venison and give me your blessing."

And Isaac said, "How is it that you have found it so quickly, my son?"

"Because Jehovah your God sent me good speed," was the answer.

Then Isaac said: "Come near to me that I may feel of you, and see if you are really my son Esau."

So Jacob went near, and his father put his hands upon him, and said: "Your voice is the voice of Jacob, but your hands are those of Esau. Are you really my son Esau?"

And Jacob answered him falsely, "I am."

Then Isaac said, "Bring the food to me, and I will eat of your venison and give you my heart's blessing."

When Isaac was through eating and drinking, he said to his son, "Come now and kiss me, my son." And he smelled of Jacob's clothes, and said, "The smell of my son's clothes is like that of a field which Jehovah hath blessed." And Isaac gave Jacob his blessing, saying:—

"May God give thee the dew of heaven,
And the richness of the earth,
With plenty of grain and new wine.
May nations bow down to thee,
And all the people serve thee.

67

Thou shalt be master over thy brothers,
And over all the family in thy mother's house.
Cursed be every one that curseth thee,
And blessed be he that blesseth thee."

As Isaac finished blessing Jacob, Esau returned from his hunt, and came into his father's tent with a dish of savory venison, saying, " Let my father arise and eat of his son's venison and give me his blessing."

" Who are you? " his father cried.

" I am your first-born son Esau," was the answer.

" Who then brought me food? And I did eat of it and blessed him! Yes, and he shall be blessed," Isaac said.

" Bless me, even me also, O my father! " Esau cried bitterly.

And Isaac said, " Your brother came with deception and has taken your blessing."

" He took my birthright, and now he has my blessing also," Esau cried. " Have you no blessing for me, too, my father? "

Then Isaac said : —

" Thou shalt dwell amid the richness of the earth,
Under the dew of heaven.
By thy sword shalt thou live,
And thou shalt serve thy brother ;
Though in due time
Thou shalt break his yoke from thy neck."

But Esau could not forgive his brother for
stealing his father's blessing.

JACOB'S JOURNEY AND HIS DREAM

In his heart Esau said: " My father is old
and cannot live long. When he is gone,
I will kill my brother Jacob, because he has
taken both my birthright and my blessing."

His mother Rebekah knew what was in
Esau's heart, and she sent for Jacob, and
said to him : " Esau is angry, and some
day he may kill you. Now, my son, listen
to my words. Flee to Laban my brother,
who lives in Haran. When Esau's anger

has passed, I will send for you to come home."

Rebekah then went in to her husband, and said: "I do not like the daughters of Heth, among whom we live. If Jacob should take one of them for his wife, as Esau has done, my life would be miserable."

And Isaac said to Jacob: "You shall not take a wife from the women of Canaan. Go to your mother's old home, and there find a wife among the daughters of your Uncle Laban. And may God bless you, as he did Abraham, and make from you a great people."

So Jacob left his home in Beersheba and started alone on the long journey toward Haran.

One night, when the sun had set, Jacob put a stone under his head and lay down on the ground to sleep. But while he slept, he dreamed that he saw a ladder set upon the earth with the top reaching to heaven.

JACOB'S DREAM

Angels were going up and down the ladder, and Jehovah stood above it, saying: " I am Jehovah, the God of your fathers, Abraham and Isaac. The land on which you are lying shall be given to you and to your children's children. They shall be as the dust of the earth in number, and shall scatter east and west and north and south. All the families of the earth shall be blessed because of them. Behold, I am with you, and will keep you wherever you go, and will bring you again into this land. I will not leave you until I have done all that I have promised."

Then Jacob awoke from his sleep, and said: " Surely, God is near, and I knew it not. This is the very gate of heaven."

In the morning, when Jacob rose to go on his journey, he took the stone from under his head and set it up for a shrine, and poured oil upon it, and worshiped there, calling the place Bethel, which means " House of God."

And Jacob made a vow, saying: "If God will be with me and lead me on this journey, and will give me bread to eat and clothing to wear, and bring me safely back to my father's house, he shall be my God. This stone that I have set up shall be God's house, and one tenth of all that he gives to me will I return to him."

Then Jacob went on with his journey.

JACOB FINDS RACHEL

AFTER many days, Jacob reached the city of Haran. In the field outside of the city he saw the well where Abraham's servant found Rebekah, Jacob's mother, many years before.

The well was covered with a large flat stone, and flocks of sheep were gathered in the field near by, waiting to be watered.

Jacob spoke to the men who were with

the sheep, and said, "Where do you come from, my men?"

"We are from Haran," they answered.

"Do you know a man in Haran by the name of Laban, the son of Nahor?" Jacob asked.

"Yes, we know him," was the answer.

"Is it well with Laban?" asked Jacob.

"It is well. See, his daughter Rachel is coming now to water her father's sheep, for she cares for them."

Jacob was glad when he saw his cousin Rachel. He went quickly and rolled away the heavy stone cover, and watered her sheep for her. And he told Rachel that he was the son of Rebekah, her father's sister.

Rachel hurried home to tell the good news that Jacob had come to Haran. And Laban ran out to meet him, and threw his arms about him, and kissed him, and brought him to his house, and said, "You are truly my blood kinsman."

Jacob had been in his uncle's home about a month, when Laban said to him: "You shall not serve me without wages, although you are my kinsman. Tell me what your wages shall be."

Now Laban had two daughters. Leah, the older daughter, was a plain girl with weak eyes. But Rachel, the younger one, was fair to look upon.

Jacob already loved Rachel, and he said to Laban, "I will serve you seven years, if you will then give me your daughter Rachel for my wife."

And Laban answered, "I would rather give her to you than to a stranger. You may stay with me."

So Jacob worked for his uncle seven years, but the years seemed only a few days to him, his love for Rachel was so great.

At the end of the seven years, Jacob said to Laban, "Give me my wife, for my time of service for her is ended."

So Laban gathered together all the men of his family and gave a great feast. In the evening, as was the custom, the bride was brought to Jacob and became his wife. A long, heavy veil covered the bride, so that her face could not be seen. But the next morning Jacob found that he had been given Leah for his wife, instead of the beautiful Rachel, and his anger was great.

"What is this you have done to me?" he cried to Laban. "Have I not served you seven years that I might win Rachel? Why have you deceived me?"

"It is not our custom that the younger daughter should marry before the older one," Laban answered. "Serve me yet seven years more, and you shall have Rachel also."

So Jacob worked for his uncle seven more years to win the wife whom he loved.

JACOB LEAVES HIS UNCLE

AFTER a time, Jacob said to his uncle, " I would go back to my own country and to my father's home. Give me my children and my wives, for whom I have served you, and let me go."

And Laban said : " Tell me what wages you would have, and you shall go. God has blessed me greatly while you have been with me. What shall I give you? "

" Give me only the spotted cattle and goats, and the black sheep that are in your flocks," Jacob answered him.

Now Laban had large flocks of goats and sheep, and herds of cattle, but he did not like to give any of them away, even though there were but few spotted and black ones among them. Ten times he promised to give Jacob his wages, and ten times he broke his promise. He secretly went through his flocks, and took out all the spotted goats and black sheep, and told his sons to drive them three days' journey away, so that Jacob might not get them.

But Jacob would not go back to his father's home empty-handed. He continued to feed and care for his uncle's flocks, and when the little calves and lambs and kids were born, he quietly took all the spotted and black ones and began to make flocks of his own.

It happened that large numbers of the little new kids and lambs were either spotted or black, so Jacob's flock grew rapidly. Laban and his sons soon saw that Jacob's flocks were larger and stronger than theirs, and they were jealous of him.

Jacob knew that he would not be allowed to take his flocks away openly. So one day when Laban was away shearing his sheep, Jacob and his family took their flocks and all their possessions, and started back to the land of Canaan.

They had crossed the river and had traveled three days toward the mountains before Laban was told that Jacob had left him. He then took his men and followed fast after them, overtaking them seven days later in the mountains of Gilead.

"What have you done?" Laban cried to Jacob. "Why have you stolen secretly away, taking my daughters like captives with you? And why did you take my household gods, the teraphim, with you? If you had told me you were going, I would have sent you away with music and mirth, with songs and the harp."

"I was afraid you would take your daughters from me," Jacob answered. "And as for the gods, if you find them with any one of us, that one shall die." For Jacob did not know that Rachel had stolen her father's idols.

So Laban went into Jacob's tent, and into Leah's, and into the tent of the two maidservants, but he did not find his images. He then went into Rachel's tent, but Rachel had hidden them, and they were not found.

Jacob was angry because Laban thought he had stolen his property and had searched the tents for them. The two men finally separated with friendly words, saying, " May God watch between me and thee when we are absent one from another."

JACOB'S GIFTS TO ESAU AND THE WRESTLING MATCH

As Jacob and his family neared Canaan, Jacob began to fear that his brother might not receive him kindly. He remembered how he had deceived Esau twenty years earlier, and he was afraid Esau might still be angry with him.

So Jacob sent messengers before him with these words to Esau: " Thus saith your servant Jacob — I have lived twenty years with Laban in Haran, and have oxen and donkeys and flocks and menservants and maidservants. I am now returning to my homeland, and I beg you to greet me kindly."

The messengers returned to Jacob, saying, "We gave your message to your brother, and he is now coming with four hundred men to meet you."

Jacob was alarmed, and he quickly divided his people, and his flocks and herds and camels, into two companies. For he said, "If Esau should attack one company, the other company might then escape."

And Jacob prayed earnestly that the God of Abraham would protect him against the hand of his brother, and would bless him and his children forever.

After a night of rest, Jacob prepared a present for Esau. He took from his flocks two hundred and twenty goats, two hundred and twenty sheep, thirty camels and their colts, fifty cattle, and thirty donkeys. He put a servant in charge of each drove, and told them to go on ahead of him, each drove going separately.

Jacob said to the servant with the first drove: " When Esau my brother meets you and asks who you are, and where you are going, and whose flock you are driving, say to him: ' The flock is thy servant Jacob's. It is a present sent to my lord Esau, and Jacob himself is coming behind us.' "

Jacob spoke the same words to the driver of the second flock, and to the third, and to all that followed, for he said, " I will soften Esau's anger with the presents sent before me, that when we meet, he may welcome me with gladness."

So the servants, with the long procession of gifts, passed on ahead. And Jacob slept that night with one of his companies. But in the night, Jacob rose and sent his two wives, with their maids, and his eleven sons, and all that he had, across the river Jabbok, where the water was shallow. When he was left alone, a strange man wrestled with him till the break of day. And when the stranger could not overcome Jacob, he twisted Jacob's thigh until it was strained. And the stranger cried, " Let me go, for the day cometh ! "

And Jacob said, " I will not let you go until you have blessed me."

" What is your name? " asked the stranger.

" It is Jacob," was the answer.

" It shall no longer be Jacob, but Israel — Soldier of God," the stranger said, " for you have wrestled with God and man and have won." And he blessed Jacob there. And Jacob called the place Peniel, meaning " Face of God." For he said, " I have seen God face to face, and my life is saved."

And as the sun rose, Jacob went limping on his way.

ESAU WELCOMES JACOB

Soon after crossing the river Jabbok, Jacob saw his brother Esau coming to meet him with four hundred men.

Jacob quickly divided his family into three groups, placing the two handmaids and their children first, with Leah and her children behind them. And behind them all, in a place of safety, were Rachel and her son Joseph, both of whom Jacob loved very much.

Jacob then went forward alone to meet his brother, bowing with his face to the ground seven times, as he came near to Esau. But Esau ran to meet Jacob, and he put his arms around him, and fell upon his neck and kissed him. And they wept for joy.

When Esau saw the women and children who were with Jacob, he said, " Who are these with you? "

" They are the family that God has graciously given to me," Jacob answered.

THE MEETING OF JACOB AND ESAU

The handmaids then came near, with their children, and bowed to the ground before Esau. And Leah and her children came and bowed low, and so also did Rachel and her son Joseph.

And Esau said to Jacob, " What is the meaning of the many flocks that I met on my way? "

" They were sent as a present, that I might find favor with my lord," Jacob answered.

" I have enough of everything, my brother," Esau said. " Keep what belongs to you."

" No, I pray you to accept my gifts, if I have found favor with you. God has dealt kindly with me, and I, too, have enough," Jacob answered. And he urged Esau, until he accepted the gifts.

And Esau said, " Let us go on with our journey. I will go before you."

But Jacob answered: " My lord knows that the children are tender, and that the flocks and herds with me have their young. If we should drive them too fast, even for one day, the flocks might die. Let my lord pass on ahead of us, and we will come on more slowly, following the pace of the children and the cattle, until we reach your place."

So Esau went back to his home in Seir, while his brother, with his flocks and his family, came on slowly. They stayed for a time at Bethel, where Jacob, twenty years before, had dreamed that he saw a ladder reaching unto heaven, with angels going up and down upon it.

Soon after leaving Bethel, another boy was born to Rachel and Jacob, and they named him Benjamin. But Rachel died, leaving Jacob sorrowing for her.

Finally, Jacob reached his old home, and found his father Isaac still living. But Isaac soon died, at the age of a hundred and eighty years. His two sons, Jacob and

Esau, then buried him with his father and mother, Abraham and Sarah, in the family cave of Machpelah.

THE COAT OF MANY COLORS

THE TWELVE BROTHERS

THERE were twelve sons in Jacob's family when he reached his old home in Canaan. From the oldest to the youngest their names were: Reuben, Simeon, Levi, Judah, Dan, Naphtali, Gad, Asher, Issachar, Zebulun, Joseph, and Benjamin. There was also a daughter Dinah.

The ten older brothers were grown men at this time, and Joseph was a tall boy, nearly seventeen years of age, but Benjamin was hardly more than a baby.

On reaching Canaan, Jacob, who was a rich herdsman, bought a portion of a field for a hundred pieces of money. Here he spread his tents, and built an altar to Jehovah.

In those days the Hebrew herdsmen all lived in tents made of camel's or goat's hair cloth. As Jacob's sons married, he gave them each a new tent to live in near his own. This soon made a large family for Jacob to care for, with his sons and their wives and their children. But the sons did the work of shepherds and herdsmen for the thousands of cattle and sheep belonging to their father.

Jacob was not always wise in showing his special love for his son Joseph, which often made the brothers jealous. Soon after returning to Canaan, Jacob made for Joseph a handsome coat of many colors, with long, loose sleeves. It was the kind of coat a young prince might wear, or the oldest son in a rich family. But Joseph was neither the oldest, nor was he a prince.

The brothers were jealous when they saw Joseph wearing his handsome coat, while they had only rough shirts or goatskin coats. It was hard for them even to be civil to the boy.

Canaan was a dry, hot country. Sometimes, for many weeks, there was no rain. Then the streams all dried up, and even the deep wells had but little water in them. At such times Jacob's sons had to take their sheep and cattle long distances from home to find grass and water. They often went to the wild, hilly country, where the sheep had to be watched carefully, lest wolves come and kill them.

Sometimes Joseph and Benjamin went to the pastures with their older brothers. Once when Joseph was with them, he saw his brothers do something wrong, and he talked with his father about it. This made the brothers angry with Joseph, for they did not want their father to know what they had done.

The men grew more and more jealous of their young brother, with his beautiful colored coat, and they were more and more unkind to him. Trouble was surely coming.

THE DREAMER

JACOB not only had many sheep and cattle, but also large fields of grain. Each year, when the grain was ripe, his sons cut it for him and tied it into big sheaves.

Joseph liked to help with the work in the grain fields. His father did not often let him go to the pastures to watch the sheep. But Joseph helped in the fields. He liked to cut the ripe grain. He liked to see how straight he could make his sheaves stand up. And perhaps he liked to play among the standing sheaves with Benjamin and the children of his older brothers.

Sometimes, when he was very tired, the boy lay down in the shade of a tall sheaf and fell asleep. And of course, sometimes he dreamed.

Joseph dreamed so much, his brothers called him the Dreamer. They did not always like his dreams.

One day, when Joseph was asleep, he had a very strange dream. When he awoke, he ran to his brothers and said : " O brothers, listen! I have had a dream. I dreamed that we were all out in the fields together tying the ripe grain into sheaves. We had each tied one sheaf, when my sheaf stood up all alone. Then your eleven sheaves stood up, too. They stood all around my sheaf and bowed low to it."

In those days people believed that dreams had meanings. If anyone had a strange dream, he always tried to find out what the dream might mean.

Joseph's brothers thought that if their sheaves bowed down to Joseph's sheaf in his dream, it meant that some day they would have to bow down to Joseph — that he would rule over them.

Of course the brothers did not like that dream.

Soon Joseph dreamed again. It would

have been better if he had not told his dream this time. But perhaps he was a little proud of it.

He said: " O father, listen! O brothers, listen! I have had another strange dream. I dreamed that the sun and the moon bowed down to me. I dreamed that eleven stars bowed down to me."

The brothers thought that the eleven stars in this dream meant themselves, and that the sun and the moon meant their father and mother. They were unhappy about the two dreams, for they did not want their young brother ever to rule over them.

Even Joseph's father was troubled; and he said to his son: " I do not like such dreams. Shall I and your mother and your brothers all bow down to you, as if you were a king? "

The brothers hated Joseph more than ever after this. They would not even say " Peace " to him, when they met him, which was the same as not being willing to say " Hello " to a brother in these days.

But Joseph's father kept the two dreams in his heart.

A NARROW ESCAPE

ONCE, in dry weather, the older brothers took their flocks fifty miles over the mountains to find grass and water. They were gone so long, their father became anxious and said to Joseph : " Your brothers are pasturing their flocks near Shechem. Go and see if they are well. See if their sheep are safe, and bring me word from them."

And Joseph answered quickly, "I will go, father." And he put on his bright-colored coat and started at once.

It was not an easy journey for a boy to take alone. The country was wild, and there were mountains that had to be crossed. At last Joseph reached the place near Shechem where the sheep had been pastured, but to his great disappointment, they were no longer there.

As Joseph walked about in the fields, a man saw him, and asked, "Whom are you looking for, my boy?"

"I am looking for my brothers," Joseph answered. "Can you tell me where they are feeding their sheep?"

"I heard them say they were going to Dothan," said the man. "The grass up there is better for the sheep, and there is water in some of the wells."

So Joseph walked fifteen miles farther on, over the hills to Dothan. His brothers saw him coming while he was still a long way off, for they knew him by his many-colored coat.

"Look! There comes the Dreamer," they said to each other. "We do not want him here. Let us kill him, and put him into a pit. We can tell his father that a wild

98

beast has eaten him. We shall see then if his strange dreams come true."

Reuben, the oldest brother, loved Joseph and did not want him to be killed. He said to the others : " We must not kill Joseph. We can put him into this dry well, but we should not hurt the lad."

Reuben knew that his brothers would go away and leave Joseph in the well. He could then return and take him out and carry him home to his father.

So the brothers took off Joseph's beautiful coat that had made them so jealous, and put him down into the pit. Then they sat on the grass to eat some food, and paid no attention to Joseph's calls for help.

Soon a company of men on their way to Egypt came along the highway. They had a long train of camels loaded with fruits and spices, which they were going to sell in Egypt.

When Joseph's brothers saw the men,

Judah said: " What good will it do us if we kill Joseph, or let him die in this pit? Let us sell him to these men, for after all, he is our brother, and we should not hurt him."

So, when the men came near with their camels, Joseph's brothers drew him up out of the well and sold him to them for twenty pieces of silver. And the boy was soon on his way toward Egypt.

SOLD AS A SLAVE

REUBEN was not with his brothers when Joseph was sold to the traveling merchants. He thought that the boy was still in the well. And when his brothers were not in sight, Reuben went back to take Joseph out of the well and carry him home to his father. But the well was empty.

"What shall I do?" Reuben cried, as he ran to his brothers. "The boy is not there. Someone has taken him away."

JOSEPH IS SOLD FOR TWENTY PIECES
OF SILVER

The brothers then told Reuben what they
had done, and they all agreed not to tell
their father. They killed a young goat and
dipped Joseph's coat into its blood, and
took the coat back to their father and said:
"See what we have found. Is it your son's
coat?"

Poor old Jacob knew the coat. When he
saw the blood on it, he cried: "This is my
dear son Joseph's coat! Some wild beast
has killed him. My boy is dead."

Jacob's sons and daughters tried to make
him happy, but he said: "I shall never be
happy again. My dear son Joseph is dead."

But Joseph was not dead. The strange
merchants, to whom his brothers had sold
him, were taking him far away from his old
home in Canaan. They came, at last, to
the land of Egypt, which seemed very wonderful to the boy who had always lived
in a tent. There were beautiful temples
and great pyramids and many cities filled

with people. It was a rich and interesting country.

The merchants were not long in selling their sweet spices. Joseph was a handsome boy, almost a man. Surely someone would buy him for a slave.

And someone did buy Joseph.

The king of Egypt had an officer in his army by the name of Potiphar. When this officer saw Joseph, he liked him so much he bought him from the merchants. Potiphar took the boy to his home to be his slave, or private servant, for he was a rich man and lived in a beautiful house.

Perhaps the first thing that Joseph was asked to do was to swing a great feather-fan during the long, hot afternoon, for Egypt was a hot country. Joseph did his work well for Potiphar. He always tried to do what was right, and God helped him every day.

Potiphar was so pleased with the Hebrew

103

servant that, as time went on, he gave him charge of his whole house and of all the other servants. And Potiphar prospered while Joseph was in his house. But he was not to stay there long.

IN AN EGYPTIAN PRISON

THINGS began to go badly with Joseph down in Egypt. Potiphar's wife did not like him. She made her husband think that he had done something wrong, and he was put into prison.

But God was good to Joseph in his trouble because Joseph did not forget God even in prison. The keeper of the prison soon became Joseph's friend. He saw that Joseph tried to do what was right, so he gave him charge of all the other prisoners, making him overseer of the whole place.

One day two new prisoners arrived. They were servants of Pharaoh, the king. One was a baker who helped to cook the king's food. The other was the butler who took the king's wine-cup to him. These men had each done something that displeased Pharaoh, so they were put into prison, and Joseph was told to look after them.

One night the two prisoners each had a strange dream. When Joseph came to them in the morning, he said: "Why do you look so sad to-day?"

The men answered, "Last night we each had a dream, and there is no one here to tell us what the dreams mean."

"Perhaps God will help me to understand your dreams," Joseph said. "Tell them to me."

So the butler told his dream to Joseph.

He said: "In my dream I saw a vine. On the vine there were three branches, and on the branches were small buds. The buds became blossoms, and the blossoms became ripe grapes. I had the king's cup in my

105

hand, so I took the grapes and pressed the juice into the cup, and carried the cup to the king."

"Your dream is clear to me," Joseph said. "The branches are three days. In three days the king will send for you and will make you his butler again. You will do the work that you used to do for him."

"But," Joseph added, "do not forget me when you are in the king's house once more. Speak to Pharaoh about me. Tell him that I was stolen from the land of Canaan. I have done nothing wrong since I came to Egypt, but my master has put me into prison. Perhaps the king will set me free."

When the baker found that the butler's dream had a good meaning, he said, "I, too, had a dream. I dreamed that I carried three baskets on my head, one basket above another. In the top basket were all kinds of cooked food for the king to eat. But the birds came and ate the food from the basket."

" This is the meaning of your dream," Joseph said to him. " The three baskets are three days. In three days the king will send for you. He will have you hanged on a tree, and the birds will eat your flesh."

THE KING'S DREAM

THE dreams of the butler and the baker came true, as Joseph had said they would. In three days the king of Egypt had a birthday. On this day he gave a great dinner for all of his servants.

The king sent to the prison and had the butler and the baker brought to him. He told the butler to take up his work again, but the baker was hanged on a tree.

When the butler went to live in Pharaoh's house once more, he forgot all about Joseph. He forgot to tell the king what Joseph had asked him to say. So Joseph stayed on as overseer in the prison. He had been there for two long years, when Pharaoh dreamed a dream.

The king dreamed that, as he stood by the river Nile, he saw seven fine, fat cows come up out of the water. The cows ate the grass on the meadows near by. He then saw in his dream seven other cows. They came up out of the water also, but these cows looked thin and hungry, and they ate up the fine, fat cows.

The king then awoke, but he fell asleep again and dreamed another dream. This time he dreamed that he saw seven large ears of corn grow on one stalk. Then seven other ears of corn grew on the same stalk, but these ears were thin and had no corn in them. And the seven thin ears ate up the good ears.

Pharaoh wanted to know the meaning of his strange dreams, so he sent for all the

wise men of Egypt to come to him, but none
of them could tell what the dreams meant.

The king's butler then remembered Joseph,
and he said: " O King, once you were angry
with me and with your baker, and you put
us into prison. While we were there, we
each had a dream, and there was a young
Hebrew in the prison who told us what our
dreams meant. His name was Joseph. He
said that after three days you would ask
me to be your butler again. But he told
the baker that he would be hanged. And
it all came to pass, just as the young man
said."

Pharaoh then sent for Joseph, and they
brought him out of the prison. When Joseph had shaved and put on fresh clothing,
he went to the king's palace and bowed
before the king.

Pharaoh looked at the handsome young
slave, and said to him: " I am told that
you understand the meaning of dreams. I

have had two strange dreams. My wise men cannot tell me what the dreams mean. Are you wiser than they? "

" It is not I, O King, but God who can tell you the meaning of your dreams," Joseph answered him. " Will you tell them to me? "

JOSEPH BECOMES A GOVERNOR

Pharaoh then told his two dreams to Joseph.

He said : " In my dream I was standing by the bank of a river. I saw seven fine, fat cows come up out of the water and feed in a meadow near by. Then seven thin, hungry cows came up out of the water. I never saw such thin cows in all Egypt. The seven thin cows ate up the seven fat cows, but they still looked as thin and as hungry as before.

" Then I awoke; but I soon fell asleep

110

JOSEPH INTERPRETS PHARAOH'S DREAM

and dreamed again. I dreamed that I saw seven large ears of corn grow on one stalk. Then seven thin ears of corn grew on the same stalk, and they ate up the seven good ears."

"Your two dreams, O King, have the same meaning," Joseph said to him. "God has told you what he is going to do. The seven fat cows and the seven good ears of corn are seven years. The seven thin cows and the seven bad ears of corn are seven other years.

"First there will come seven years when the corn and the grass will grow well. Your people will have all they want to eat. Then there will be seven years of famine. No rain will fall. The corn and the grass will not grow. Your people will be very hungry."

Joseph then said to Pharaoh: "Choose a wise man, O King, and make him ruler over your land. Tell him to save one fifth of all the grain that grows during the seven good years. The people will then have food to eat during the seven years of famine."

"Can we find a wiser man than this Joseph?" Pharaoh said to his servants. "God tells him what to say and what to do. I will make him ruler over Egypt."

Pharaoh then called for Joseph, and said to him: "There is no man in all Egypt so wise as you. You shall not go back to the prison. You must be ruler over my land. My people shall do what you say. I alone shall be above you."

Taking a ring from his own hand, the king put it on Joseph's, and said, "See, I have set you over all the land of Egypt."

Joseph was then dressed in rich clothing, and the king put a gold chain about his neck. Joseph rode in a beautiful chariot next to that of the king, and the people bowed low to him and did what he told them to do.

Joseph was thirty years old at this time. He married a beautiful wife, and they had two fine sons.

During these days, Joseph must have thought often of his old father in the land of Canaan, and of his brother Benjamin, whom he loved so much. And perhaps he thought of the ten older brothers, who had sold him to the strange merchants for twenty pieces of silver. Did they ever think of him now?

THE GREAT FAMINE BEGINS

FOR seven years the grain grew well in Egypt. The people had more than they needed to eat. Joseph traveled up and down the land ordering barns to be built and filled with the extra grain. Every city in Egypt had many barns filled with it.

So much grain was saved that at last it was like the sand by the sea; it could not be measured.

When the seven good years were over, the seven bad years began. No rain fell, and there was famine in all the land.

The people of Egypt soon ate up all their food, and they went to Pharaoh for help. But Pharaoh said to them: "Go to Joseph. Do what he tells you to do."

And Joseph opened the great storehouses where the extra grain was kept, and sold it to the people, so they all had enough to eat. People began to come to him from other countries, too, to buy grain, for there was little to eat in their own lands. The famine was everywhere.

Joseph's father and eleven brothers were still living in the land of Canaan. It was many years since the brothers had sold Joseph to the strange merchants. They did not know what had become of him. They thought he was dead.

The famine was great in Canaan, and Joseph's brothers did not know where to find food for their children to eat. At last Jacob said to his sons : " I have heard that there is grain in Egypt. Go down and buy some, so that we may have bread, and may not all die."

So Jacob's ten older sons started for Egypt. But Benjamin, the youngest boy, stayed at home with his father. Jacob feared that something might happen to the boy, if he went with his brothers.

It was a long journey to Egypt. The men rode upon donkeys, and carried empty sacks to be filled with grain. They took money with them, also, to pay for the grain.

Joseph was nearly forty years old at this time. He was Governor of the whole of Egypt, and it was he who sold grain to all the people who came to buy.

When the brothers arrived in Egypt, they went straight to the great Governor and bowed very low to him. They bowed with their faces down to the ground, for this was their custom in greeting people of high rank.

Joseph knew at once that the ten men were his brothers, but they did not know him, and he did not tell them who he was. He remembered the strange dream that he had when he was a boy. In the dream his brothers' sheaves of grain had bowed down to his sheaf. And now here were his brothers all bowing down to him!

JOSEPH PUTS HIS BROTHERS
INTO PRISON

JOSEPH wished to find out if his brothers were selfish and unkind, as they had been when he was a boy, so he pretended not to know them. He spoke roughly to them, saying, "Who are you? And where do you come from?"

"We have come from the land of Canaan," said the men. "We want to buy food from you."

"You are enemies," said Joseph. "You are spies in our land. You want to see how weak we are, so that you may make war upon us."

"No, no! We are not spies," said the brothers. "We are honest men. We have come only to buy food, for there is none in our land."

But Joseph said again, "No, you are enemies. You have come to spy out our land."

Then they answered him : "My lord, we are all brothers. Our father had twelve sons. The youngest one is with him now in the land of Canaan, and one is dead. We only want to buy food for our families."

"I will know if you speak the truth," Joseph said. "One of you shall go home to Canaan, and shall bring the youngest son down to me. The rest of you shall stay here until he comes. Then I shall know if what you say is true."

So the ten brothers were bound and put into prison for three days. On the third day Joseph went to them and said: "I will do the right thing by you, for I serve God. Only one of you shall be bound and kept here. The rest of you may return to your home, and carry grain for your hungry families. But you must bring your youngest brother back to me. Then I shall know that you are honest men, and you shall not die."

The brothers were sad, and they said to each other: "This evil has come upon us because of what we did to our brother Joseph, years ago. We put him into a pit and would not listen to his cries. Then we sold him to strange merchants, and we have never known what they did with him."

"I told you not to hurt the lad," Reuben said to the others. "But you would not listen to me, and now God is giving us what we deserve."

The men did not know that Joseph could understand their language. He had spoken to them always in Egyptian and another man told them what he had said. But Joseph did understand every word that his brothers spoke. He saw that they were sorry for their unkindness to him when he was a boy. This made him both glad and sad, and he had to go away from them and cry.

MYSTERIOUS MONEY

JOSEPH soon dried his eyes and came back to his brothers, but he was not ready to let them know who he was until they had brought Benjamin to him. He told his servants to tie one of the men and put him into prison. He then told the servants to fill the other men's sacks with grain, and to put into the sacks the money that each man had paid for his grain, and to give the men food to eat on the way home.

119

When the brothers had loaded their sacks of grain on their donkeys, they started for their home in Canaan, but without Simeon. They stopped on the way to rest, and one of the men opened his sack to get food for the donkeys. To his great surprise, in the top of the sack he found the money that he had paid for the grain.

" Look, brothers! " cried the man. " My money has come back to me. See, here it is in my sack! "

When the men saw the money, they all trembled and were afraid, for no one knew how it came to be in the sack. They did not dare to return to Egypt and tell the ruler what they had found. They were afraid he would put them all into prison again. So they hurried on toward Canaan.

When they reached their home, the brothers told their father all that had happened. " The Governor of Egypt spoke harshly to us," they said. " He thought we had come to spy out the land. We told him that we were honest men. We said that our father had twelve sons, that the youngest was with his father in the land of Canaan, and that one son was dead. But the ruler of the land said he would find out if we spoke the truth. So he bound our brother Simeon and kept him in prison. He then sent us home with food, and said that if we would bring our youngest brother back to him he would let us have Simeon again, and that we might buy more grain in his land."

When the brothers finished telling their story, they opened their sacks to pour out the grain, and there, in the top of each sack, was the money they had paid for it. They did not know what it could mean.

"What is going to happen to me?" Jacob cried aloud. "My children are being taken from me! Joseph is gone! Simeon is gone! And now you want to take Benjamin also."

But Reuben, the oldest son, said : "I have two sons, father. If I do not bring Benjamin back to you, they shall both die."

But Jacob said : " My youngest son shall not go with you. Joseph is dead. If anything should happen to Benjamin, my heart would break. He shall not leave me."

THE FAMINE IN CANAAN

THE famine grew steadily worse in the land of Canaan. In Jacob's family there were sixty-six people to feed, for his sons were all married, and there were children and grandchildren. There were the servants also, who waited on the family, and the men who cared for the flocks. These people all lived in tents set around Jacob's tent.

Jacob was a rich man. He had plenty of gold and silver to buy food for his large family, though, during the great famine, there was little food to buy.

The grain that Jacob's sons had brought from Egypt, the first time they went down, did not last long. When it was nearly gone, Jacob said to his sons, " Go again to Egypt and buy us more food."

But Judah said to his father: " The ruler of Egypt told us that we should never see his face again unless we brought our youngest brother with us. If you will allow Benjamin to go with us, we will go down and buy food. If Benjamin does not go with us, we will not go down, for we could not see the ruler without him."

" Why did you tell the ruler that you had a younger brother? " Jacob cried. " You knew that it would kill me to lose him."

" The man asked us if our father were still alive," the sons answered him, " and if we had another brother. How could we know that he would tell us to bring our brother down to him? "

Then Judah said to his father: " Send

the lad with me and I will go and fetch food for you and for our children. I will take care of Benjamin, and will bring him back to you safe and well. If anything happens to him, I will bear the blame forever. We could have gone to Egypt and back again by this time if we had not waited so long."

Jacob then said: " Well, if Benjamin must go, take him. And take a present to the ruler also. Take some of the best fruits of the land. Take honey and nuts and perfume. And take twice as much money with you as you took before, besides the money that was returned in your sacks. It may have been put there by mistake."

When his sons were ready to start on their journey, Jacob cried: " May God make the ruler of Egypt kind to you! May Simeon be set free and Benjamin be brought back to me! If my children are taken from me, I shall surely die!"

A FAMILY DINNER

So Jacob's nine sons took their presents and their money and their brother Benjamin, and went down a second time to Egypt. Again they stood before the Governor of the land and bowed low to him.

When Joseph saw Benjamin with his other brothers, he was very happy. He called for the steward who was in charge of his house, and said to him, "Take these men to my home and prepare a fine dinner, for they shall eat with me at noon."

The steward did as he was told, but the men were afraid. They said to each other: "The Governor knows about the money that we found in our sacks. He thinks that we stole it, and has sent us to his house. He will take our donkeys away from us and make us his slaves."

Then they said to the steward: "O sir, some time ago we came down to Egypt and bought grain. When we reached home and opened our sacks, we found the money that we had paid for the grain in the top of each sack. We do not know who put it there, but we have brought it back. We have brought more money, too, to buy more food."

But the steward would not take the money. He said to the men, "Your God must have sent it to you as a gift. You paid me for the grain. Do not be afraid." And he brought Simeon to them, who had been kept in Egypt while his brothers went home to Canaan with food.

The steward then gave the men water to wash their feet, and food for their donkeys, and he took them into Joseph's house and told them that they were to eat with the Governor at noon.

When Joseph came in, his brothers brought their presents to him, bowing with their faces to the ground.

126

" Is your father still living, and is he well? " Joseph said to the men.

And the brothers answered, " Our father is still living, and he is well." And again they bowed very low.

When Joseph saw Benjamin, he said, " Is this your youngest brother, of whom you spoke to me? May God bless you, my son."

He then left them quickly and went into his own room and cried for joy, for he had found his dear brother Benjamin. But Joseph soon washed his face, and came out of his room, and his brothers did not know that he had been crying.

" Set on the bread," he said to his servants.

So the servants set three tables, one for Joseph, one for his brothers, and one for the Egyptians who lived in Joseph's house. It was against the law for the Egyptians to eat at the same table with Hebrews.

When the eleven brothers were seated at their table, they saw that the oldest brother had the first seat, the next oldest had the second seat, and so on down to Benjamin, and they wondered who could have known how to seat them in that way.

Joseph served his brothers from the food on his own table, but he put five times as much on Benjamin's plate as on the others. And they ate and drank and had a merry time.

THE SILVER CUP

THE eleven brothers enjoyed their dinner with the great Governor of Egypt. When the dinner was over, the Governor said quietly to his steward: " Fill these men's sacks with food, and in the top of each sack put the money that they have paid us for the grain. In the sack of the youngest brother place my silver cup, and put in his money also."

The steward did as he was told. And the next morning, as soon as it was light, the men loaded the sacks of grain on their donkeys, and started for their home in Canaan.

They had gone only a little way from the city when Joseph said to his steward : " Go, follow the men, and ask why they have returned evil for good — why they have taken my silver cup."

So the steward followed the men quickly, and said, " Why have you stolen my master's silver cup? "

The brothers were surprised, and answered: " Why do you ask such a question? We would not steal your master's cup. Did n't we bring back to him the money that we found in our sacks? How can he think we would steal silver or gold from his house? If the cup is found with any of us, that one shall die, and we will all be your slaves."

But the steward said, " If one of you has

the cup, that one shall be my slave, but the rest shall not be blamed."

Each man then quickly took down his sack and opened it.

The steward looked first into the sack of the oldest brother. Then he looked into the sacks of each of the other men, until he came to Benjamin's.

Alas! the silver cup was found in Benjamin's sack.

The brothers were now very much afraid. They loaded their donkeys once more, and went sadly back to the city with Joseph's servant. They went straight to the Governor's palace and fell down on their faces before him on the ground.

When Joseph looked at his brothers, he said: "Why did you do this thing? Did n't you know that you would surely be found out?"

"What shall we say, my lord?" cried Judah. "What shall we do that we may

130

not be punished? God has found our sin.
We are all my lord's slaves, even the one
in whose hand the cup is found."

Joseph then said : " I will not be hard with
you. Why should I keep you all? The
one in whose sack the cup was found shall
be my slave. The rest of you may go home
in peace to your father."

But the brothers could not leave Benjamin
behind. Judah had given his promise to
take the boy back safe and well to his father.
He had said that he would bear the blame
forever, if he did not do so.

JUDAH'S PLEA AND JOSEPH'S SECRET

JUDAH came nearer to Joseph, and said :
" Oh, do not be angry with me, my lord!
We know that you are as great as the king
of the land. Let me speak a little to you,
and do not be angry.

" When we first came down to Egypt,

you asked if we had a father. We said that our father was an old man, that our youngest brother was with him in the land of Canaan, and another brother, whom our father loved very much, was dead.

" You told us to bring our brother down for you to see, and we said that our father would die, if the lad left him. You then told us we should never see your face again, if we did not bring our brother to you. We went home and told our father your words, but he said that Benjamin should never leave him.

" At last our grain was gone, and our father asked us to go again to Egypt and buy a little food. We told him we could get no food unless Benjamin was with us. And he said : ' In my old age, my wife Rachel gave me two boys. We named them Joseph and Benjamin. The boy Joseph is gone. If you take the other boy from me I should die with sorrow.' "

132

JOSEPH MAKES HIMSELF KNOWN TO HIS
BROTHERS

Then Judah said: " My lord, I promised my father that if he would let Benjamin go with us to Egypt, I would take care of the lad, and if harm came to him, I would bear the blame forever. Oh! let me stay and be your servant. Let Benjamin go home with his brothers. If we go home without the lad, my father will surely die."

Joseph loved his brother Judah for offering to give himself in place of Benjamin. He could not keep his secret from them any longer.

So Joseph sent his servants out of the room, and was left alone with his eleven brothers. Then Joseph wept. And his weeping was heard in Pharaoh's palace. " I am your brother Joseph!" he cried. " Is my father still alive? "

The brothers were afraid and could not answer him, for this was the first time he had spoken to them in their own language.

" Come near to me," Joseph said to them.

And they came near, though they were trembling with fear.

"I am Joseph your brother, whom you sold into Egypt. Do not be troubled that you sold me. God sent me here to save the lives of many people. For two years there has been a famine in all lands. For five more years there shall be neither ploughing nor harvest.

"Pharaoh has made me ruler over all the land of Egypt. Make haste! Go back to my father and say to him: 'Your son Joseph is ruler over all Egypt. He bids you come down to him. You shall live on the best of the land, you and your children and your flocks and all that you have. Joseph will care for you through all the years of famine.' Go! Tell this to my father. Make haste! Go quickly, and bring him down to me."

Joseph then put his arms about his brother Benjamin's neck and wept for joy.

And Benjamin wept, too. And Joseph kissed each of his brothers, and they talked of many things together.

A HAPPY JOURNEY

Now when Pharaoh heard that the brothers of his Governor had come to Egypt, he was glad. He told Joseph to give them wagons to bring their wives and their little ones down to Egypt, and food to eat on the way.

Joseph also gave a change of new clothing to each of his brothers. But to Benjamin he gave five times as much as he did to the others, and three hundred pieces of silver. And to his old father he sent twenty donkeys loaded with bread and grain and other good things from Egypt.

Joseph then told his brothers to go quickly, and not to quarrel on the way.

So the brothers left Egypt, and came again to the land of Canaan. When they saw their father, they cried: "Father! Father! Your son Joseph is still alive. He is ruler over all the land of Egypt. It is he who has sold us our grain."

Jacob could not believe what his sons said. It was too wonderful to be true, and his heart grew faint. But his sons told him all the kind words that Joseph had spoken to them. They showed him the wagons that Pharaoh had sent to take him and their families back to Egypt. They showed him the food, and the new clothing, and the three hundred pieces of silver.

When Jacob saw all these things, he believed, and his heart was glad. He said: "It is enough. Joseph, my son, is yet alive. I will go and see him before I die."

So Jacob left his old home in the land of Canaan, and started, with all that he had, for Egypt. They had not gone far, when they came to an altar that Jacob's father Isaac had built many years before.

Jacob stopped at the altar to pray, and God spoke to him in the night, saying, "Jacob! Jacob!" And Jacob answered, "Here am I."

And God said: "I am the God of your fathers. Do not fear to go down to Egypt. I will make your family a great nation. I will go with you and will surely bring you back again."

So Jacob and all his family went on to Egypt. It was a long procession. There were herds of cattle, and flocks of sheep, and wagons filled with food and women and children. Jacob's sons and grandsons numbered sixty-six men. Counting Jacob and Joseph and Joseph's two sons, there would soon be seventy Hebrew men in Egypt.

Jacob sent his son Judah ahead to tell Joseph that they were coming. And Joseph rode in his beautiful chariot as far as Goshen to meet his father, and he put his arms about his father's neck and wept for joy.

"Now I am ready to die!" Jacob cried. "My son Joseph is still alive, and I have seen his face once more."

Joseph then said to his father and to his brothers: "I will go and tell Pharaoh that my father and all my family have come to me. I will tell him that you are shepherds, and that you have brought your sheep with you."

THE GREAT RULER

So Joseph and five of his brothers went to Pharaoh, and Joseph said: "I have done as you told me, my lord. My father and brothers have come from the land of Canaan to live in Egypt. They have brought their cattle and sheep with them. They are now in the land of Goshen."

Pharaoh asked the brothers what kind of work they had done. "We are shepherds, my lord," they answered him. "The famine is great in Canaan, and we have come to Egypt to find pasture for our flocks."

And Pharaoh said to Joseph: "Your father and your brothers shall live in Goshen, the best pasture-land in all Egypt. If they are good workers, you may put them in charge of my cattle, for the Egyptians do not like to be shepherds."

Joseph then brought his father, who was a hundred and thirty years old, to meet Pharaoh. And Jacob blessed Pharaoh.

The famine lasted seven long years. Little or no rain fell during all that time. The sun was very hot. Grasshoppers ate every green thing that grew. There was hunger everywhere.

The only grain to be had was in Pharaoh's storehouses. Joseph, who was in charge of the storehouses, became more and more powerful. Little by little the Egyptians brought all their money to him for food. At last, when their money was gone, they said : " Give us bread, or we shall die! Our money is gone."

Joseph then said to them : " I will give you bread in exchange for your cattle. Bring them to me."

So the Egyptians brought their cattle, and their horses, and their flocks to Joseph, and he gave them food for another year. But when the year was ended, they said : " We cannot hide from my lord that our money is gone. We have given our cattle, and our sheep, and our horses to you in exchange for food. We have nothing left but our land and ourselves. We beg you to buy us and our land, that we may live. Then we, and all that we have, shall belong to Pharaoh."

So Joseph bought the land of the Egyptians for Pharaoh. Each man sold his field willingly, as nothing could grow while there was no rain.

Joseph then sent the people to the cities

141

to live, where they could be more easily fed from the storehouses of grain. People came from all corners of the land and filled the cities.

At the end of the seventh year of famine the rain came, and things began to grow again. Joseph said to the people: "You and your land now belong to Pharaoh. But you may live on the land, and I will give you seed to sow. Each year, when harvest comes, you shall give one fifth of all your grain to Pharaoh. The rest you may keep for your families, and for seed."

The people knew that it was Joseph who had kept them alive during the long years of famine, and they were thankful to him.

"We will do as you say," they said, "for you have saved our lives."

THE FAMINE ENDED

AFTER the famine was over, Joseph's father and brothers continued to live in that part of Egypt called Goshen. They and their children and their grandchildren became a great many people. They had large herds of cattle and many sheep, and they were rich men once more.

Jacob had lived in Goshen seventeen years when he knew that he must soon die, for he was a hundred and forty-seven years old. He called his son Joseph to him, and said: " If you love me, do not bury me in Egypt when I die. Take my body back to the land of Canaan, and bury me there in the cave at Hebron, with Abraham and with Isaac my father."

And Joseph promised to do as his father wished.

Jacob then blessed Joseph and his two sons, and he blessed his other children also.

143

When he died, he was given a great funeral. Nearly all of the Hebrew people, except the little children, took the long journey back to Canaan with him. Many Egyptians went, too. And they placed Jacob's body in the family cave of Machpelah at Hebron, as he had wished.

After the brothers had returned to Egypt, their fear of Joseph came back again. They said to each other: "Now that our father is gone, Joseph will surely punish us for the wrong that we did him when he was a boy."

So they went to Joseph, and said: "Before our father died, he asked you to forgive us because we sold you to the strange merchants. Now we beg you again to forgive us!" And they fell down before him, and cried, "We are your servants. Be kind to us!"

Joseph was sad when he saw that his brothers were still afraid of him.

"Do not be afraid of me," he said to

them. "You wanted to do me harm, I know, but God took care of me. He brought me into Egypt so that I might save the lives of many people. I will care for you and for your little ones as long as I live. Do not fear."

Joseph spoke so kindly to his brothers, they were no longer afraid of him. He kept his promises, and he cared for them and for their families in the land of Egypt until he died, at the age of a hundred and ten years.

This was the boy to whom his father gave a beautiful colored coat, like that of a young prince. He was the Dreamer who was laughed at and unkindly treated by his older brothers, but they did later bow down to him, as they would bow to a real king. Joseph was a princely boy and a kingly man.

THE BURNING BUSH

JACOB'S GRANDCHILDREN
BECOME SLAVES

JACOB's children and grandchildren and great-grandchildren lived in Egypt many years. They were called the Children of Israel, or the Israelites, because one of Jacob's names was Israel.

The Israelites expected to go back to their home in Canaan sometime, as God had promised they should, but the life in Egypt was so pleasant they did not want to leave.

After a time, however, the king of Egypt, who had been so kind to them, died, and a new king took his place. The new Pharaoh had never known Joseph, and did not care for his people.

The proud Egyptians had almost forgotten how Joseph saved their country during the seven years of famine. They never liked the

Israelites, perhaps because they were shepherds and farmers, and lived in tents, and wore rough clothes.

The Egyptian people lived in beautiful cities, in well-built houses. They bathed often, and wore fine clothes, and did not like to do rough, hard work.

There were seventy Hebrew men, besides women and children, who went down to Egypt from Canaan during the famine. They had large families, and after a few years there were many hundreds of them.

Most of these Hebrews continued to live in Goshen, which was the best pasture-land in Egypt, though some of them went to other parts of Egypt to live. They were strong men, and they did much heavy work for the Egyptians.

Pharaoh soon saw that the Hebrew people were increasing fast. He began to fear that they would some day become greater in number than the Egyptians.

At last he said to his officers : " See, there are more men among the Children of Israel than there are among us. They are stronger and larger than we are. If there should be a war, they might join our enemies and fight against us, or they might leave the country. Then who would build our cities, and look after our sheep and cattle? We must set taskmasters over them to watch them, and to keep them at work."

So the Children of Israel were made to work very hard. They dug clay, and made bricks, and built storehouses and cities. If one of them stopped to rest, an Egyptian taskmaster drove him back to his work again. They were treated like slaves. They worked in the fields, too, and were forced to give a large part of their crops each year to the Egyptians.

In spite of such treatment, the Hebrews continued to increase in number. At last Pharaoh became so anxious about this, he spoke to some women who cared for the Israelite babies. He told the women that every boy baby born to the Hebrews, after that day, must be killed, though the girl babies might live. But these good women would not kill the Hebrew babies, even though the king of Egypt commanded them to do so.

HOW ONE BOY WAS SAVED

WHEN Pharaoh found that the Hebrew boy babies were not being killed, as he had ordered, he sent for his Egyptian officers, and said to them: "Every boy baby that is born to the Israelites must be thrown into the river Nile. Their people are growing too great and too strong. They may join our enemies and make war upon us."

About this time a beautiful baby boy was born into the home of a good Israelite and his wife. The baby's mother knew that an

Egyptian officer might come and take her baby away from her, so she hid him in her home for three long months.

At last the baby grew so big and so noisy, she could not hide him any longer. How could she save her precious boy? She was a wise mother, and she knew that God would help her. She believed that if Pharaoh's daughter could see her beautiful boy, such a princess would be able to save him.

So the mother made a little basket-boat, and laid her baby in it. She then placed the basket among some rushes, near the bank of the river, where Pharaoh's daughter often came to bathe.

The baby's sister Miriam, who was about twelve years old, was sent to watch the basket and to see what happened. Miriam had a brother, a few years younger than herself, whose name was Aaron. Miriam and Aaron loved their baby brother, and wanted to save him. So the sister hid quietly behind some tall rushes, where she could watch the little boat.

It was not long before Miriam saw Pharaoh's daughter walking by the river with her maidens. The princess noticed the queer little basket-boat floating among the rushes, and sent one of her maids to get it for her.

To their great surprise, when they opened the basket, the princess and her maidens found a beautiful baby boy lying in it. Probably the baby was both hungry and frightened, for he was crying.

" What a beautiful baby! " exclaimed the princess. " He is a Hebrew child. He must be taken care of."

From her hiding place, Miriam heard what was said, so she ran to the princess, and cried eagerly, " Shall I go and find an Israelite woman to nurse the baby for you? "

" Yes, yes, go! " said the king's daughter.

So Miriam ran and found her own mother, and brought her to the princess.

The princess said, "Take this child and nurse him for me, and I will pay you wages."

So the mother took her baby back to her own home, and cared for him. No one could harm her boy now, for Pharaoh's daughter wished him to be saved.

The little boy grew fast, and at last the princess sent for him to be brought to the palace to live with her, like an own son.

"I will name the child Moses," she said, "which means 'drawn out'; for I drew him out of the water."

MOSES, THE YOUNG PRINCE

THE palace of the Egyptian king was very beautiful.

Moses, the Hebrew boy, grew up among the nobles of the land, as the son of the princess. He learned much more than he could have learned among his own people, for there were wise teachers among the

Egyptians, and the princess gave him the best that could be had.

But Moses knew that he was not really the son of the Egyptian princess. His own mother had cared for him during the first years of his life, and she had told him that he belonged to the Children of Israel. She told him, too, about Abraham and Isaac and Jacob, and how Joseph came down to Egypt and saved the people from starving during the long famine. Then she told him how the Egyptians had later forgotten all that Joseph did for their country, and how they had made slaves of his people.

While Moses was growing up in the palace of the Egyptian king, he remembered his mother's stories. He saw how hard the Israelites were made to work. He saw how cruelly the Egyptians treated them, and he grew more and more troubled by it all.

In his heart Moses was an Israelite, and he longed to help his own people. The

Israelites were trying to serve the God of their fathers, while the Egyptians worshiped idols and animals.

When Moses became a man, he often went out and watched the Hebrews at their work. Perhaps he was trying to plan how he might help them in their trouble. He was living like a prince in the palace of the king who was treating the Hebrews so cruelly. Surely he ought to be able to help them, and perhaps to set them free.

Unfortunately, the Israelites did not trust Moses, and would not follow his advice, because he had been brought up in Pharaoh's palace, and they did not trust any of Pharaoh's people.

One day, while Moses was watching some Hebrews at their work, he saw an Egyptian master beating one of the workmen. This made Moses angry, and in trying to save the Hebrew, he struck the Egyptian too hard, and killed him.

Moses thought no one saw what had happened. But the next day, when he tried to separate two Hebrews who were quarreling, one of them said, " Who made you a prince and a judge over us? Would you kill me, as you killed the Egyptian yesterday? "

Moses then knew that Pharaoh would soon hear of what he had done, and that he would be killed for trying to help his own people. He must get out of the country at once.

So Moses left Egypt, and went to the land of Midian, beyond the Red Sea, and no one knew where he had gone.

A NEW HOME

It was a long, hot journey from Egypt to Midian. Moses was tired when he reached a well where the Midian people watered their flocks.

It was the end of the day, and Moses was

sitting by the well resting, when some girls came to draw water for their sheep. They were the seven daughters of Jethro, a priest and farmer who lived near by.

The girls drew water from the well to fill the long troughs where their sheep could drink. While they were doing this, some shepherds came along and rudely drove the girls' sheep away from the troughs, so that their own flock might drink first.

When Moses saw what was happening, he quickly came to the help of the girls, and drew their water for them, while the shepherds had to wait.

Because of the help which the stranger had given them, the girls reached home earlier than usual. Their father said to them, "How is it that you have come back so quickly tonight?"

"An Egyptian stranger drove the shepherds away from the well, and watered our sheep for us," they answered eagerly.

"Where is the man?" asked their father. "Why did n't you bring him home? Go, ask him to come and eat with us."

Moses came gladly, and when Jethro found that the man had no place to stay, he invited him to live with them, and to help with the care of his flocks.

Moses was forty years old when he came to Midian to live. He was happy in the priest's home and he married one of the seven daughters, whose name was Zippora, meaning "the little bird."

Much of Moses' life up to this time had been spent in the palace of the Egyptian king. He had learned all that the Egyptians could teach him, and had had everything that he wanted. He had been a great prince, but now he was to be a simple shepherd. For forty years he had lived in a gay, wicked city. For the next forty years he was going to live in the wild, beautiful country. It was a great change, but Moses was a good man, and was happy wherever God led him.

Instead of his fine Egyptian clothes, Moses now wore the rough skin-coat of a shepherd. When he was out with his sheep, he carried a long shepherd's staff. He wore sandals on his feet.

Much of the time Moses lived alone, for he took his flocks wherever the best grass was found. He often went with them to the mountains, and many nights he slept on the bare ground, under the shining stars.

Moses liked the shepherd's life. He felt nearer to God in the beautiful country than he ever had in a great city.

A STRANGE VOICE

YEAR after year slipped by. While Moses was watching his sheep among the mountains in Midian, his people were still suffering in Egypt. They were the slaves of the

Egyptian ruler. They were forced to do the hardest kind of work, and were cruelly treated.

Moses often thought of their suffering, and longed to do something to help them. But what could one poor shepherd do?

At last the old king of Egypt died, but a new king, who was just as cruel to the Israelites, took his place.

In their great trouble, the Children of Israel cried to God for help. Some of them thought that their God had forgotten them, but they soon found that he had not.

About this time, over in Midian, Moses was taking his sheep a long way from home to find grass for them to eat. As he came near a high mountain, which was called Horeb, he saw something strange. A bush on the mountain side seemed to be on fire.

Moses watched the bush for a long time, and at last he said to himself, " I will go and look at this strange thing. The bush

162

seems to be on fire, but it does not burn up."

As he came nearer to the burning bush, he heard a voice calling his name, " Moses, Moses! "

And he answered, " Here am I."

Then the voice said, " Do not come near unless you take your shoes from off your feet. You are standing on holy ground."

So Moses took off his sandals, and came nearer to the burning bush.

He then heard the voice saying: "I am the God of your father, the God of Abraham, and of Isaac, and of Jacob. I have seen the suffering of my people in Egypt. I have heard their cry for help. I have come to set them free from their Egyptian masters. I will lead them back to their own land, the land of their fathers, which is flowing with milk and honey. Come now, and I will send you to Pharaoh. You shall lead my people out of Egypt."

163

But Moses said, "How can I, a simple shepherd, do this great work?"

And God answered: "I will surely be with you, and will help you. When you have led my people out of Egypt, you shall bring them to this mountain, and they shall worship me here. Then you shall know that God has been with you."

But Moses was still afraid to go, and said: "If I go to the Children of Israel, and tell them that the God of their fathers has sent me, they will say, 'Who is this God? What is his name?' They have suffered so much, and have fallen so low, I fear they have forgotten their God. They will not believe what I tell them."

THE WONDERFUL SIGNS

Moses thought that the Children of Israel might be worshiping Egyptian idols by this time. He had been away from them for forty years. If he should go back now, what should he say to them? How could he give them God's wonderful message?

He was thinking of these things, when the voice from the burning bush came to him again, saying: "Tell the Children of Israel that my name is I AM — the One who is always living. Go to them and say that the God of their fathers has sent you. Tell them that I have seen their trouble, and will bring them out of Egypt into their own land, flowing with milk and honey.

"Take the leaders of Israel with you, and go to Pharaoh, and ask him to let your people go. Say that you must worship Jehovah, your God, on a mountain three days' journey away."

But Moses' only answer was, "Pharaoh will not listen to me."

"I will make Pharaoh listen to you, until he lets your people go," came the voice from the burning bush.

But Moses was still afraid to go. He asked for some sign to show to the Children of Israel and to the Egyptians, to prove to them that God had sent him.

So God said to him, " What is it that you have in your hand? "

" It is a rod. It is my shepherd's staff." Moses answered.

" Throw it on the ground! " was the command.

So Moses threw his rod on the ground, and suddenly it became a serpent.

Moses was afraid of the serpent, and started to run away, but God said, " Do not fear. Put out your hand, and take the serpent by the tail."

Moses did as he was told, and the serpent became a rod in his hand once more.

God then said to Moses, " Put your hand into your bosom under your coat, and take it out again."

Moses put his hand under his coat, and

when he took it out, it was as white as snow, like the hand of a leper. He looked at it with great fear, but God said to him, " Put your hand into your bosom once more."

Moses did so, and when he took it out this time, his hand was well. It was no longer a leper's hand.

And God said to Moses : " If the Israelites do not believe what you tell them, show them the first sign. Let your rod become a serpent, and then a rod again. If they still do not believe your words, show them the second sign. Change your hand into a leper's hand, and then make it well, as it was before. And if they still will not believe you, take some water from the river Nile and pour it over the dry land, and the water shall turn as red as blood. Fear not. Go and speak my words to your people and to the Egyptians."

THE RETURN TO EGYPT

Moses dreaded to go back to Egypt, even though he had three wonderful signs to prove that God had sent him. He thought that he was not an easy talker, and that the Israelites would not follow him. He was afraid to speak to Pharaoh.

So God said to Moses: " Was it not I who made man's mouth? Go, and I will teach you what to say."

But Moses answered: " O Lord, I am not able to do this thing. I pray you send some other man."

Then God said: " Your brother Aaron shall go with you. He will help you, and will speak for you. He is coming now to see you. Tell him all that I have said to you, and go back together to your people. I will be with you, and will help you. Take your rod, and show the signs that I have given you."

168

At last Moses said that he would go.

During all the time that Moses had been talking with God, he was on Mount Horeb near the burning bush. He now took his flocks back to Jethro, his wife's father, and said to him, " I must go back to Egypt, and see if my people are still alive."

Jethro said that Moses might go, and gave him his blessing.

So Moses took his wife Zippora, and his two sons, and started at once for Egypt. Zippora and the children rode upon a donkey, but Moses walked, carrying his wonderful staff in his hand.

They had not gone far when they met Moses' brother Aaron, who was coming to Midian to see him.

Probably the brothers had not seen each other since Moses left Egypt, many years before. Moses told Aaron all that had happened to him, and together they traveled back to Egypt to save their people from slavery.

When they reached Egypt, the brothers went directly to Goshen, where most of the Israelites still lived. They found the Egyptians treating the Israelites cruelly.

Aaron called the Elders of the land together, and told them all that God had said to Moses on the mountain in Midian. He said that they must ask Pharaoh to let them all go to the Mountain of God to worship there.

Moses then showed the three wonderful signs that God had given him. He threw his rod on the ground, and suddenly it became an angry serpent. When he picked the serpent up by the tail, it became a rod again. He then put his hand under his coat, and drew it out white and sick, like the hand of a leper. He put it a second time under his coat, and it came out strong and well. Then he dipped some water from the river Nile, and poured it on the ground, and it became as red as blood.

When the people saw the strange signs, and heard God's message to them, they were both afraid and glad.

"God has seen our trouble, and is going to set us free at last!" they cried.

NEW BURDENS

WHEN Moses and Aaron had finished telling their story to the Children of Israel, they took the Elders of the land, and went to the palace and stood before the king, as God had commanded them to do.

They did not, at first, ask Pharaoh to let their people leave Egypt never to return. They asked only for a holiday.

They said: "The God of the Israelites has commanded his people to go a journey of three days unto his mountain. We would hold a feast and worship him there. Our God says to you, 'Let my people go, that they may serve me!'"

But Pharaoh said: "Who is this God? Why should I obey him? What are you doing to call your people away from their work? Go back to your tasks, and let your people alone. They think that they should have a holiday because they have not enough work to do. I will make their tasks heavier."

So Pharaoh sent for his taskmasters, and said to them: "The Children of Israel are idle. They want to go away and worship their God. Give them more work to do. Let them find their own straw for their bricks. But see that they make as many bricks each day as they did when the straw was found for them. Then they will no longer listen to lying words from such men as these."

The work done by the Israelites, at this time, was largely making bricks and putting up walls and buildings for the rulers of Egypt. The bricks were made by mixing

172

straw with clay to hold the clay together. These bricks were then baked in the sun, until they were hard and ready for use.

The taskmasters had always furnished the straw that was needed for this work, but now the Israelites must find straw for themselves. This meant that they must go out and gather it from the cut grain fields in the country. And if they did not make as many bricks each day as they did before, they were cruelly beaten by their masters.

The poor Israelites soon saw that instead of being set free, as Moses had promised, their lives were harder than ever.

Some of their leaders went to Pharaoh and begged for help, but Pharaoh only laughed at them, and said: "You are idle! You are idle! That is why you have asked to go away and worship your God. Go, now, and work! You shall have no straw given you, but you must make as many bricks each day as you made before."

As the Israelite leaders went sadly away from Pharaoh's palace, they met Moses and Aaron. They blamed the two men for interfering with their lives and making their burdens heavier.

" May God judge you! " they cried out to them. " You have done us harm instead of good. You promised to set us free, but you have only made our sufferings greater. Go, and leave us! "

THE MAGICIANS

MOSES was sad when he found that Pharaoh had increased the burdens of the Israelites. He cried to God once more to help them, and again God promised that he would surely lead his people out of Egypt, back to their home in Canaan. But God said that Pharaoh's heart was hard, and that he would not let the people go at once.

God then told Moses to go again to Pha-

174

raoh, and show him the wonderful signs that had been given him. So Moses and Aaron went again to Pharaoh's palace, and asked him, in God's name, to let their people go.

Pharaoh said to them, " Can you show me a sign that your God has sent you? "

Here was Aaron's chance. He quickly threw his rod down before Pharaoh, and in a moment it became a serpent.

Pharaoh was astonished. The Egyptians liked tricks of magic. There were magicians who performed for Pharaoh nearly every day, so he now sent for two of them to come and show their power.

The two magicians, Jannes and Jambres, came, bringing their rods with them. They had heard much about the wonderful trick that the two Israelites were performing, so they came prepared.

They threw their rods proudly on the floor, and soon there were two more snakes creeping about. But suddenly, the serpent that

175

was Aaron's rod swallowed up the other two snakes, and it became a rod in Aaron's hand once more.

All this made the great Pharaoh laugh, but his heart was hard, and he would not listen to Moses and Aaron.

So God spoke to Moses again, and said: "Pharaoh goes down to the river to bathe each morning. Go, and meet him there. Tell him that the God of the Hebrews has sent you to say, 'Let my people go, that they may serve me!'

"If Pharaoh will not listen to you, Aaron shall stretch his rod over the rivers, and over the streams, and over the pools, and over the ponds of water, and the water shall become red like blood. Even the water that is in dishes of wood and stone shall be like blood."

Moses and Aaron then did as God commanded, but Pharaoh would not listen to them. And Aaron stretched out his rod,

THE WATERS OF EGYPT ARE TURNED INTO
BLOOD

until all the water in Egypt became as red as blood, and it remained so for seven days.

The fish in the rivers died. There was a terrible smell over all the land. The people could not drink the water. They had to dig new wells, or die of thirst.

Pharaoh's magicians wanted to show that the God of the Israelites had no more power than they, so they took fresh water from the wells that had just been dug, and turned it red, as Moses and Aaron had done.

Again Pharaoh laughed. Even though he saw the suffering of his people, he would not let the Children of Israel go.

This was the first great plague.

FROGS AND MORE FROGS

MOSES gained courage. He was no longer afraid of Pharaoh. Again he and Aaron went to the royal palace and stood before the king.

Moses said to the king: "The God of the Israelites says to you, 'Let my people go, that they may serve me.' If you do not let them go, frogs shall come up out of the river in great numbers and cover your land. The river shall swarm with them. The frogs shall get into your house, and into your bedchamber, and even into your bed. They shall enter the houses of your servants, and of all your people. The people shall find frogs in their ovens, and in the bowls where they are kneading their bread. You shall find them on your bodies, you and your people and your servants."

Moses then said to Aaron: "Stretch your rod over the streams, and over the pools, and cause frogs to come upon the land of Egypt."

So Aaron stretched his rod over the waters of Egypt, and frogs came up and covered the land.

Again Pharaoh's magicians tried to do

179

the same thing, and they, too, brought frogs upon the land. So Pharaoh believed that his magicians were as powerful as the God of the Israelites. But the magicians could not send the frogs away. There were frogs everywhere. The people could not walk, or eat, or sleep, with any comfort.

At last Pharaoh could stand it no longer. He called for Moses and Aaron, and said: "Ask your God to take these frogs away from me and from my people. I will then let your people go, that they may serve him."

Moses said to Pharaoh, "At what time shall I ask to have the frogs taken away?"

"Let it be to-morrow," Pharaoh answered.

"It shall be as you say," Moses replied. "You will then know that no one is so powerful as our God. To-morrow the frogs shall be taken away from your house, and from the houses of your servants and your people. They shall remain only in the river."

Then Moses and Aaron left Pharaoh, and Moses cried to God to destroy the frogs that had been sent upon Pharaoh. And God heard his call.

The next day, all the frogs that were in the houses, and in the courts, and in the fields of Egypt, died. The people gathered them together in heaps and buried them.

But when the frogs were gone, Pharaoh changed his mind. He remembered that frogs often came up out of the rivers of Egypt and troubled the people. Perhaps it would not happen again for a long time. He was not going to let the Children of Israel leave the country for so small a thing. Who would make bricks and build cities for the Egyptians, if he let the Israelites go?

No, the Israelites must stay and do their work.

LICE AND FLIES

PHARAOH had failed the second time to keep his promise to the Israelites. And God said to Moses, "Tell Aaron to strike the dust of the earth with his rod, and the dust shall become lice."

So Aaron used his rod, and everywhere there were lice. They were on the people, as well as on the animals, in all the land of Egypt.

Again the magicians tried their skill, but they did not succeed this time. They were too frightened to even pretend they had succeeded, and they went to Pharaoh, and cried, "This is the finger of God!"

But Pharaoh's heart was hard. He would not listen even to his magicians.

So God said to Moses: " Rise up early in the morning, and go down to the river where Pharaoh bathes. Stand before him and say: 'Our God says to you, "Let my people go, that they may serve me. If you do not let them go, swarms of flies shall come upon you, and upon your servants, and upon your people. The houses of all the Egyptians shall be filled with flies. The ground where you walk shall be covered with them. But in the land of Goshen, where the Hebrews live, there shall be no flies. God will draw a line between your people and his people, so that you may know that he is the God of the earth. To-morrow shall this sign come." ' "

And when to-morrow came, the sky was dark with flies. There were great clouds of them. They spoiled the food. They carried sickness. They were in all the houses of Egypt. But in Goshen, where the Hebrews lived, there were no lice or flies.

At last Pharaoh called for Moses, and said, " You may worship your God here in this land. Why should you leave the country? "

But Moses answered : " When we worship

183

God, we make an offering to him. Our offerings are oxen and sheep, which the people of Egypt worship. The Egyptians would be angry, and might kill us, if we offered their gods as a sacrifice to our God. No, we must go three days' journey into the country and offer sacrifice to God on his mountain, as he has told us."

Then Pharaoh cried: "Go, and worship your God! But go not far away. And before you go, command these terrible flies to leave us."

Moses answered: "I will go out and pray to God that the flies be sent away from Pharaoh and his people to-morrow. But you must not deceive us again. You must let us go, as you have promised."

The next day there were no more flies to be seen in Egypt, not one. But when they were gone, the proud Pharaoh only laughed, and the Israelites did not go on their journey.

THE GREAT SICKNESS

AGAIN God spoke to Moses, and said: "Go
to Pharaoh once more and say to him:
'The God of the Hebrews says to you — Let
my people go, that they may serve me.'

"Tell Pharaoh that if he does not let the
Children of Israel go, but holds them here in
Egypt, a great sickness shall come upon his
cattle. The cattle in the fields shall die.
His horses and donkeys and camels and
sheep shall all have the terrible sickness.

"But there shall be a difference between
the cattle of the Israelites and the cattle of
the Egyptians. Nothing shall die that
belongs to the Children of Israel, for they
are my people. To-morrow shall this thing
happen."

And so it did. The next day great numbers of Pharaoh's cattle and horses and
camels and sheep were taken sick. Many
of them died.

Pharaoh then remembered what Moses had said about the cattle belonging to the Children of Israel, so he sent some of his men to see if anything had happened to them. The men found that the cattle of the Israelites were all alive and well. Not one had died.

It would seem as if Pharaoh would surely listen to the request of the Israelites now, but he hardened his heart again, and would not let them go.

God then said to Moses and Aaron: " Go to Pharaoh's furnace and fill your hands with the ashes. Then stand before Pharaoh and sprinkle the ashes toward heaven in his sight. The wind shall blow the dust of the ashes over all Egypt, and wherever it touches a man or an animal, it shall make a sore boil."

So the two men went to the furnace and filled their hands with ashes. Then they went and stood before Pharaoh, and Moses sprinkled the ashes upward toward heaven in his sight, and the wind took the dust and carried it to all parts of Egypt.

The dust of the ashes was like poison. Boils came on all the people whom it touched. The animals, too, were covered with sore boils. There was no one who could heal them.

Even the magicians were so covered with the terrible boils they could not come out to beg Moses for help.

Probably Pharaoh himself was suffering as much as his people were, but he was not yet ready to yield and let the Children of Israel go. There were thousands of them. They were his slaves. He must not lose them. He could never get the Egyptian people to do all the hard and heavy work that these Hebrew slaves were doing for him.

Pharaoh's heart was still hard, and even this last great plague was not enough to change it.

A TERRIBLE HAILSTORM

As Pharaoh still would not yield, God spoke to Moses again and said: " Rise up early in the morning. Go, stand before Pharaoh and say again to him: 'The God of the Hebrews says to you — Let my people go, that they may serve me.'

" If Pharaoh does not let the Children of Israel go, I will pour out plagues upon him and upon his people, until they know that there is no one like me in all the earth. To-morrow, at this time, a great storm shall come upon Egypt. Never has there been so great a storm since Egypt was a nation.

" Let Pharaoh send quickly to the fields, and have his servants put their cattle under cover, those that did not die of the great sickness. Every man and animal found in the fields when the hail begins shall surely die."

Many of Pharaoh's people were now afraid

188

of the God of the Hebrews. When they heard this last message from him, they sent quickly to the fields and brought their cattle and servants under cover. But some, who did not believe in the strange warning, stayed with their cattle in the fields.

It did not often rain in Egypt. Sometimes there was not even a shower for several years. So it was hard for the people to believe that the terrible storm, of which Moses talked, would really come. Anyway, they would wait and see.

The next day God said to Moses: "Stretch forth your hand toward heaven, and hail shall come upon all the land of Egypt, upon man and upon beast and upon all the green things in the field."

So Moses stretched his rod upward, and black clouds covered the sky. Then thunder and hail and lightning came down upon Egypt. Only in the land of Goshen, where the Children of Israel lived, there was none.

It was a terrible storm. The thunder rolled. The lightning sent fire upon the ground. The rain poured down. And with the rain came hail, which the Egyptians had never seen before.

The hail cut down everything that was growing in the fields. It ruined the fruit trees. The flax and the barley, that were nearly ripe, were cut down to the ground. Only the wheat, that was not yet grown, was safe.

At last Pharaoh was really frightened. In the midst of the noise of the storm, he sent for Moses and Aaron and cried: " I have sinned. My people and I are wicked. But God is good. Entreat him to take this great thundering and hail away from us. We will then let your people go."

Moses answered : " I will do as you say. When I have gone out of the city, I will pray God to stop the thunder and the hail. You will then see that the earth is God's. But you will not fear him."

Moses was right. When Pharaoh saw that the rain and the hail and the thunder had stopped, he only laughed at the Israelites again, and would not let them go.

AN ARMY OF LOCUSTS

Once more Moses and Aaron went to Pharaoh's palace and said to him: "How long will you refuse to let God's people go, that they may serve him? If to-morrow you still refuse, locusts shall come and cover your land, so that you cannot see the ground. They shall eat every green thing that was not killed by the hail. Your houses shall be filled with locusts, and the houses of your servants and of all the Egyptians.

"There have been locusts in Egypt many times before, but neither your fathers nor your fathers' fathers ever saw such swarms of locusts as shall come upon you to-morrow."

191

When they had given their message, Moses and Aaron turned and left the palace without saying another word.

Pharaoh's servants, who heard what the two men had said, now spoke boldly to their king. They said: "How long shall we be made to suffer? Let the men go, that they may serve their God. Do you not know that Egypt is already destroyed?"

Pharaoh saw that he must do something. So he sent for Moses and Aaron to come to him again, saying to them angrily, "How many of you would go and serve your God?"

"We would all go," Moses answered. "We would take our young and our old, our sons and our daughters, our flocks and our herds, for we must hold a feast unto God."

"Evil be with you!" cried Pharaoh. "Shall I let you all go, and take your children with you? Not so! But if your men would serve God, they may go."

Then Pharaoh commanded his servants to drive Moses and Aaron from his palace.

Pharaoh knew that if the wives and children went with the Hebrew men, none of them would ever come back again. But the Israelite men did not want to leave Egypt alone. They meant to take their families and their cattle with them, and they did not mean to return.

So, at God's command, Moses stretched forth his rod once more, and a strong east wind began to blow. It blew all day and all night.

In the morning, the people of Egypt saw swarms of locusts being brought from the east by the wind. The ground was soon black with them. They covered the fields and the trees. They ate up everything that had not already been killed by the hail, until there was not a green field left in all the land of Egypt.

When Pharaoh saw what had happened, he

called for Moses and Aaron to come quickly, and he said to them : "Now I know that I have sinned against God and against you. Forgive me only this once more. Entreat your God to save me from this death."

So Moses prayed God to save Pharaoh once more. And suddenly there came a strong west wind, which took the locusts, and drove them into the Red Sea. There was not one locust left in all the land of Egypt.

THICK DARKNESS

Do you think Pharaoh let the Children of Israel go, when the great swarms of locusts were blown into the Red Sea?

No, indeed! He hardened his heart and again forgot his promises. The trouble was over, so why should he let his Hebrew slaves go? He needed their help in building his great cities and walls. It would take something more than swarms of locusts to make Pharaoh give up the Israelites.

So God spoke again to Moses, and said: "Stretch out your hand toward heaven, and I will send darkness over the land of Egypt. It shall be a thick darkness that can even be felt."

Moses did as God commanded, and a great darkness settled down over all Egypt. It may have been caused by a heavy sand-storm, blown from over the desert.

For three days and three nights there was no sun, and no moon, and no stars. The people could not even see each other. They could not move from their places. But in the homes of the Children of Israel in Goshen it was light.

As Pharaoh sat in the thick darkness of his palace, he called to Moses, in great fear: "Go, and serve your God! Take your little ones with you. But your flocks and your herds you must leave behind."

Moses answered Pharaoh: "Our cattle shall go with us. Not one hoof shall be left behind. We need them to offer as sacrifice to God. We do not yet know what God will ask of us."

Pharaoh was angry at this. "Begone from me, and beware never to see my face again," he cried, "for on that day you shall die."

And Moses answered him, "You have spoken truly. I will never look upon your face again."

Egypt was no longer a gay and beautiful land. Week after week, terrible things had been happening, one after another.

First, the water in all the rivers and lakes had been turned red, like blood, and all the fish had died.

Then frogs came up out of the river and covered the land. They went into people's houses, and got into their beds.

196

MOSES BEFORE PHARAOH DURING THE
PLAGUE OF DARKNESS

Then there were lice, like the dust on the ground in number, and such swarms of flies that no one could either eat or sleep.

After that, a terrible sickness came upon the cattle and upon all the animals, and many of them died.

Then the people all had boils.

Next came a great hailstorm, with thunder and lightning.

And then an army of locusts came and ate up every green thing that the hail had not already cut down.

Finally, there were three days of black darkness.

The proud people of Egypt were sick and frightened. Their cattle were killed. Their fertile country was almost ruined. But their cruel ruler would not listen to the voice of God, and give the Hebrew slaves their freedom.

THE FINAL WARNING

WHILE the Egyptians were suffering from the terrible plagues, the Israelites were living in safety, not far away in Goshen.

The Egyptians saw that the God of the Israelites was watching over his people. They thought that if they brought rich gifts to him, God would be kind to them also. So they took gold and silver and jewels from their temples, and brought them to the Hebrews, hoping to win the favor of their God. They brought many precious things of every kind, until the Hebrews were rich in these treasures.

Moses had now become a great man in the sight of Pharaoh's servants, and of all the Egyptian people. They feared his power, and wished that Pharaoh would listen to him.

Finally, God spoke to Moses again, saying: "Only one more plague shall come upon Egypt. Pharaoh will then let my people go. He will even drive you out of his land. Tell the people to make ready to leave, for the time shall soon come."

Moses had hoped that he might never see Pharaoh's face again, but he now had another message to give to him.

So Moses went to the palace and stood before Pharaoh and said: "Thus saith Jehovah our God: 'At midnight, an Angel of God shall pass through the land of Egypt, and the oldest child in every family shall die, from the first-born of Pharaoh, who is sitting on the throne, to the first-born of the maidservant, who grinds your flour. Even the first-born of all the cattle shall die. But the Children of Israel shall not be harmed. So shall you know that God cares for us.'"

Moses then left Pharaoh in great anger, for Pharaoh's heart was still hard. He would have his own way, and he would not let the people go.

God had told Moses what the Israelites should do, if Pharaoh would not yield to this last request. So he hurried back to his own people and called the elders of the land together.

Moses said to the elders: "Get yourselves ready, for a long journey is before you. Let every family kill a lamb and prepare a supper. If the lamb is too much for a small family, join with your neighbor's family, and roast the lamb together.

"Kill your lamb in the early evening, and sprinkle its blood above your door and on each side of it. Do not leave your house again until morning, for the Angel of God shall pass through Egypt this night, and all the first-born in the land shall die. Only those houses where there is blood on the door-posts will the Angel of Death pass over, and there the first-born shall not die.

"This day shall be remembered among us as the day of the Passover. Go, make ready!"

THE LAST GREAT PLAGUE

THERE was great preparation that day among the Children of Israel. Lambs were killed. Blood was sprinkled on the door-posts. Bread was baked without yeast, as there was no time to raise it.

At last everything was ready. The members of each family gathered in their own house, and ate their supper hastily.

Although it was night, the people were dressed ready for a journey, with their shoes on their feet, clothing tied about their waists, and staffs in their hands.

At about the hour of midnight, a terrible thing happened. Moses' warning to Pharaoh came true. The Angel of Death passed through Egypt and entered every home where there was no blood on the door-posts.

In each home the first-born child died. Even Pharaoh's own son was not spared, nor the sons of the prisoners in the dungeon.

202

There was a great sound of weeping and fear.

Pharaoh called loudly for Moses and Aaron, and said to them: " Get you gone from among my people! Go, serve your God, as you have asked. Take your flocks and your herds and all your people and be gone! And ask a blessing for me also."

The Egyptian people were now so anxious for the Israelites to leave their land, they gave them everything that they wanted for their journey, and urged them to make haste, saying, " Go, or we shall all be dead men! "

So the Children of Israel put their kneading troughs, filled with unbaked bread, on their shoulders; they took their household goods and the gifts from the Egyptians, and left the land of Goshen.

It was a great army of people. The men went on foot, driving their cattle and herds before them, while the children and the women rode on camels and donkeys.

It had been at least a hundred and fifty years, perhaps even four hundred years, since Joseph's father and brothers came down to Egypt to get food during the seven years of famine.

There were seventy Hebrew men who came to Egypt at that time. Now there were many thousands who were leaving. They were going back at last to their old home in Canaan, as God had promised they should, and they were taking the body of Joseph with them.

God led the great procession with a pillar of cloud by day and a pillar of fire by night, so that they might be guided both by day and by night.

The fleeing Israelites hoped to go around the northern end of the Red Sea, and soon leave Egypt behind them. But they came to an Egyptian wall, with soldiers guarding the gates.

The Israelites knew that the soldiers would

shoot at them with their bows and arrows, and many might be killed, if they tried to leave Egypt that way, so they turned south toward the mountains, by the shore of the Red Sea, to decide what to do. Some of the weaker ones had already begun to wish that they had never tried to leave Egypt at all.

THE WONDERFUL ESCAPE

BACK in Egypt there was great weeping and sorrowing for many days. The oldest son in every home lay dead. No one cared what was happening to the Children of Israel. They were glad to have Moses out of the way, where he could not harm them any more.

But at last Pharaoh heard that his slaves were wandering in the mountains near the Red Sea, and he began to wish that he had not let them go. Who would serve the proud Egyptian people now that the Israelites were gone? He must get them back at once.

So Pharaoh ordered his war chariot to be made ready. He called for six hundred of his best captains, with their war chariots. Then, with all the soldiers of Egypt, he started in haste after the Children of Israel.

The many hundreds of horses and chariots made a great noise, which the Israelites heard a long way off. When they saw Pharaoh's army coming after them, they were alarmed. They had been slaves so long they could not fight, and besides, they had nothing to fight with.

They cried loudly to Moses: "Why have you brought us out of Egypt to die in the wilderness? It would have been better to serve the Egyptians, than to die here at their hands."

But Moses said quietly to the people: "Fear not! Be still, and God shall save you. These Egyptians, whom you see to-day, you shall not see again. God will fight for you. Fear not."

It was early evening. The Egyptians were tired after their long chase. They saw that the Israelites could not get away from them, for they were shut in between the mountains and the sea. So Pharaoh's army lay down for a night of rest, before driving their slaves back to Egypt.

But Moses was praying to God for help, and God said to him: "Lift up your rod, and stretch out your hand over the sea, and the water shall be divided. Speak then to the Children of Israel, and tell them to go forward. So shall they pass to the other side on dry ground."

Moses lifted up his rod over the Red Sea, and a strong east wind arose. The wind blew hard all night and the water in the shallow sea was blown back, making a safe path to the other side for the Children of Israel.

The Angel of God, who had led the Israelites, now came and stood behind them. The pillar of cloud, also, was removed from before them, and separated their camp from the camp of the Egyptians, so that they could not see each other all night. But a light from the cloud shone forward and lighted the way for the Israelites.

So the Children of Israel passed safely across the Red Sea, while the Egyptians slept.

THE LOST EGYPTIANS

THE cloud that had hidden the Children of Israel from the Egyptian army all night lifted toward morning. To his great surprise, Pharaoh saw his thousands of slaves nearing the other shore of the Red Sea. There was no time to go around by the safe road and drive them back. He must follow them quickly, or they would be out of his reach in another country.

THE CROSSING OF THE RED SEA

So Pharaoh, with his army of chariots and men, plunged after the Israelites. But the chariot wheels soon began to stick in the sand. Some of the wheels came off. The horses could not pull.

Pharaoh's captains cried out in great fear: "Let us fly from these Israelites. Their God is fighting with them and against us!"

But it was too late. They could not fly. Their chariots were stuck on the muddy bottom of the Red Sea, and the Israelites had reached the other shore.

Then God spoke again to Moses and said: "Stretch forth your hand over the sea, that the waters may come again upon the Egyptians, upon their chariots, and upon their horsemen."

So Moses stretched forth his hand, and the strong wind that had been blowing from the east all night changed and blew from the other direction, and the water in the sea flowed back to its place.

The proud and cruel Egyptian king, and his great army, were all drowned. Not one of them escaped.

So God saved the Children of Israel that day from the Egyptians, and they believed anew in his greatness and goodness, and in Moses their wise leader. Together they sang a song of triumph and praise to Jehovah their God.

The song is often called, "The Song of Moses and Miriam." Moses led the men in the singing, while his sister Miriam, and the other Israelite women, answered with singing and dancing and the playing of timbrels.

It had been more than eighty years since Miriam had watched her baby brother, as he lay in his little basket-boat near the shore of the river Nile. God had saved the child's life then, so that he might later on, when he grew to be a man, save his people from bondage.

This is a part of their song : —

"I will sing unto Jehovah, for he hath triumphed
  gloriously;
The horse and his rider hath he thrown into the
  sea.
Jehovah is my strength and song,
And he is become my salvation.
This is my God, and I will praise him;
My father's God, and I will exalt him.

"The enemy said : I will pursue, I will overtake,
I will divide the spoil;
My desire shall be satisfied upon them;
I will draw my sword, my hand shall destroy them.

"Thou didst blow with thy wind; the sea covered
  them;
They sank as lead in the mighty waters.
Who is like unto thee, O Jehovah, among the gods?
Who is like thee, glorious in holiness,
Fearful in praises, doing wonders? "

THE PILLAR OF CLOUD

DAYS OF WANDERING

AFTER their wonderful escape in crossing the Red Sea, Moses led the Israelites toward the mountain where God had spoken to him from the burning bush.

They had to cross a hot, desert country, which was wild and rough. Mountains of bare rock rose all about them. They could find but little food, and there were few springs of fresh water.

The water which the Israelites had brought from Egypt in skin sacks was soon gone, and the people grew very thirsty.

At last, after traveling three days through this hot, dry country, they came to some small springs, and they all began to drink eagerly. But to their great disappointment, the water in the springs was bitter with salt. No one could drink it.

" It is bitter! What shall we drink? " they cried loudly to Moses.

Moses called upon God for help. And God showed him a certain kind of tree, and told him to cut it down, and throw it into the water.

Moses did so, and immediately the water in the springs became fresh and pure, and the people drank all they wanted of it. They named the place " Marah," which means " bitterness," because of the bitter water which they found there.

While the Israelites were resting at Marah, God promised them that if they did not forget him, but obeyed his commands, they should not have any of the terrible sicknesses that had come upon the Egyptians. They stayed at Marah long enough to bake cakes from the dough which they had brought from Egypt in their kneading troughs. Then they filled their skin sacks with fresh water, and started once more on their journey.

They had traveled only two or three hours, however, when they came to a place where there were seventy palm trees and twelve springs of fresh water. They called the place " Elim," which means " the trees." To be sure, there were only a few trees, but they must have seemed like a beautiful forest to the tired people who had just crossed the hot desert.

Their tents were set up, and they camped for a time near the cool springs. But after a short rest, they were traveling once more. Again they passed through a wild, hilly country and across sandy plains where almost nothing could grow.

It was a long procession, and they moved slowly. There were thousands of cattle and sheep, and many more thousands of men and women and children.

Six weeks had passed since they left the land of Egypt. The grain and other food which they had brought with them was nearly gone. The Israelites feared that they might starve to death, and again they began to find fault with Moses and Aaron.

They cried: "It would have been better to have died in the land of Egypt, where we had plenty to eat. You have brought us out into the wilderness to kill us all with hunger!" For they had forgotten God's promise to care for them.

GOD'S GIFT

But God had not forgotten his promise to the wandering Israelites. He spoke to Moses and said: "I have heard the complaints of the Children of Israel. Speak to them, saying: At evening you shall eat flesh, and at morning you shall be filled with bread. So shall you know that I am Jehovah your God."

Now it happened that when evening came, a large flock of quails flew over the camp of the Israelites. The men brought the quails down with their bows and arrows, until there were enough for all to eat.

In the morning, when the dew was gone and the people came out of their tents, they saw small white flakes lying all over the ground. It looked like a heavy white frost, and the people cried, " What is it? What is it? "

" It is the bread which Jehovah has given you to eat," Moses answered them. " Gather as much of it as you need for yourselves and your families. But do not take more than you can eat in one day, for it will not keep. God will give you more to-morrow, and every day."

So the Israelites called the white flakes " Manna," which means " God's gift."

Every morning after this, during their long wanderings, the Children of Israel gathered the small white flakes from the ground. They gathered as much as they needed for one day only. But on the sixth day of each week they gathered enough for two days, so that they might rest on the Sabbath day. On the sixth day, every family baked or boiled enough manna for the next day, and it did not spoil.

The manna was delicious to eat. It tasted like wafers made with honey.

Once some of the people forgot to gather extra manna on the day before the Sabbath, so they went out early the next morning to gather it, but they found there was none on the ground. In this way the Israelites learned that God wished them to rest on the seventh day, and not do unnecessary work. They were learning, also, to trust him for their daily food, though they found that it was never given to them without some work on their part.

It took a long time to teach the Hebrew people all that they needed to know before they could become a great nation. They had been slaves for so many years, they would have been no match for the strong people who lived in Canaan, if they had gone up there when they first left Egypt.

They wandered in the wilderness, among the mountains and the deserts, for forty long years before God led them into their Promised Land. During all those years they had manna to eat every day.

Aaron gathered a potful of the manna to keep, so that their grandchildren and great-grandchildren might see the kind of bread that God gave to them when he led them out of Egypt.

TROUBLE IN THE WILDERNESS

It was a hard life for the Israelites, wandering year after year in that hot, wild country. There was seldom enough food for them or for their cattle to eat, and water was so scarce they were often thirsty.

Once, when the people could find no water, they went to Moses and cried: "Give us water to drink! Why have you brought us out of Egypt to kill us and our children and our cattle with thirst?"

Moses turned to God, and said: "What shall I do for these people? They are ready to stone me."

And God said: "Take with you the elders of Israel, and go on ahead of the people. In your hand take the rod with which you smote the river. Go to Mount Horeb and there smite the rock till water shall come out of it, that the people may drink."

And Moses did so in the sight of all the elders, and a stream of fresh water gushed from the rock. The people filled their skin water-sacks, and gave water to their sheep and their cattle. And again they knew that God was caring for them.

But the wanderers had many other troubles, besides the lack of food and water.

MOSES STRIKES WATER FROM THE ROCK

There was a fierce tribe of Arabs, called the Amalekites, that often came among them and stole their sheep and killed their men.

The Hebrews were a peace-loving people, and did not wish to fight. So the Amalekites had no fear of them, and troubled them more and more.

At last, Moses saw that something must be done. He called for Joshua, a brave young Hebrew, and said to him: "Choose some of the best of our men and go out and fight the Amalekites. To-morrow I will stand on the top of the hill, with the rod of God in my hand to give you help."

So Joshua and his men went out to meet the Amalekites, while Moses and Aaron and Hur watched the fighting from the top of a hill near by.

It happened that, whenever Moses lifted up his hands, the Israelites drove the Amalekites back with the edge of their swords.

But if Moses dropped his hands, the Amalekites won in the fighting.

When Aaron and Hur saw this, they brought a stone for Moses to sit upon, and they stood, one on each side of him, holding up his aching arms until the sun had set and the evening came.

So Joshua and his men won the battle that day against the Amalekites, and drove the troublesome Arabs away.

THE HOLY MOUNTAIN

At last the caravan reached the land of Midian, where Moses had spent so many years caring for his father-in-law's sheep.

During the trouble in Egypt, Moses sent his wife, Zippora, and her two children back to her father Jethro, where they would be out of danger.

Jethro had heard how God led Moses and the Israelites safely out of Egypt, and of their wonderful escape from Pharaoh. The old priest was anxious to see his people once more, so he took his daughter, and her two sons, and went to the plain near Mount Horeb, where the Israelites were encamped.

When Moses heard that his father-in-law had come, he went out to meet him, and knelt on the ground before him, and touched the earth with his forehead. Moses kissed his father-in-law's hand, then he rose and kissed him on both his cheeks, and invited him to his tent, where each asked the other about his welfare.

Moses told Jethro of the terrible plagues that had come upon Pharaoh and the Egyptians, and how, at last, the Israelites had escaped from their long bondage.

Jethro rejoiced in their escape and cried: "Blessed be Jehovah who hath delivered you out of the hand of the Egyptians and out of the hand of Pharaoh! Now I know that Jehovah is greater than all gods."

Then they all worshiped God together, with burnt offerings and sacrifices, after which they had a great feast.

The elders of Israel all sat down with Moses and Aaron and Jethro, and a league of friendship was formed between the tribe of Jethro and the Hebrews, which was never broken.

Jethro helped Moses to organize the government of the Hebrew nation, by appointing judges to look after the complaints and needs of the people. During the first three months of their travel, Moses had looked after everything himself, but it was too much for one man to care for so many people, and he was glad to divide a part of the work among his judges.

At last, Jethro went back to his home, and the Israelites settled down on the great plain at the foot of Mount Horeb, where they stayed for eleven months.

There was better pasturage and more

water in the narrow valleys leading away from this plain than they had found since leaving Egypt. To one side rose the rugged Mount Horeb, which they called "The Mount of God," for it was here that Moses had talked with God in the burning bush, when he was pasturing his sheep near by.

The mountain rose precipitously for nearly two thousand feet above the plain. The people were not allowed to go near it, for it was holy ground. It had long been a holy mountain to the wandering Arab tribes, who worshiped their moon-god Sin here, and who called one of its peaks "Sinai." But never had anything so wonderful happened on Sinai as the Hebrews were soon to see.

THE GOLDEN CALF

ONE day Moses went up the holy mountain, and God spoke to him, saying: " Go, say to the Children of Israel: ' You have seen

228

what I did to the Egyptians, and how I brought you, as on eagles' wings, into safety. If you will obey my voice and keep my covenant, you shall be my own people, a holy nation, for all the earth is mine.' "

So Moses called together the elders of Israel and gave them God's message. And all the people shouted, " We will do what Jehovah has told us to do!"

Now on the third morning after this, a thick cloud settled over Mount Sinai, with loud thundering and lightning. Smoke rose from the mountain, as from a great furnace, and the whole mountain quaked.

Everyone in the Israelite camp trembled with fear. Then a voice like a loud trumpet called Moses to come to the top of the mountain. And Moses went.

For forty days and forty nights, he did not come back. During all that time, the mountain was hidden from view by a thick cloud. The people began to fear that Moses was dead. Aaron could not quiet their fears. They forgot the promise they had made to Jehovah. They thought their God had forsaken them.

In wild excitement, they went to Aaron and cried : " Up, make us gods which shall go before us. As for this Moses, the man who brought us up out of the land of Egypt, we do not know what has become of him."

Men and women and children then broke off their golden earrings and other ornaments, and brought them all to Aaron. And Aaron melted the gold, and shaped it into a golden calf, like the images they had seen in Egyptian temples. He then built an altar before it, and said to the people, " To-morrow we shall have a feast to the Lord," hoping that in their hearts they would worship the true God.

On the morrow, the people rose up early and offered burnt offerings and peace offerings on the altar before the golden calf.

Then they sat down to eat and to drink, after which they rose up to dance and to play.

This was what they were doing, when, after forty days of absence, Moses came down from the mountain and entered the camp. He brought with him two tablets of stone, on which were written the laws which God had given him to guide his people. And here were these people worshiping a golden calf, such as the Egyptians worshiped!

In his great anger, Moses threw the two tablets of stone to the ground and broke them into many pieces. Then he pulled down the golden calf, and burnt it with fire, and ground it to powder, and scattered the powder over the water, which he made the people drink.

Moses now called for volunteers to put down the rebellion, saying, "Whoever is on Jehovah's side, let him come to me!"

The sons of the tribe of Levi were the only

ones who came. It was a small tribe, but
the men were brave and loved God.

Moses commanded them to take their
swords and go from gate to gate in the
camp, and kill all who did not accept
Jehovah as their God.

That night three thousand men lay dead.

THE TEN LAWS

AGAIN Moses went to the top of Mount Sinai
and talked with God, while the cloud covered
the mountain. Moses begged God to forgive the sins of his people, and not to cast
them off forever. God promised that he
would stay with them, and that his Angel
should go before them and lead them to
the Promised Land. Only those who had
sinned against him should be punished.

When Moses came down from the mountain, his face and eyes were shining with joy,
and the people could hardly look upon him.

232

MOSES BEARING THE TABLES OF STONE FROM
MOUNT SINAI

He brought with him two more tablets of stone, on which were written the same laws that were on the first tablets.

God said to them: "I am Jehovah thy God who brought thee out of the land of Egypt, and out of the house of bondage.

THOU SHALT HAVE NO OTHER GODS BUT ME.

THOU SHALT NOT MAKE FOR THYSELF A GRAVEN IMAGE.

THOU SHALT NOT TAKE THE NAME OF JEHOVAH THY GOD IN VAIN.

REMEMBER THE SABBATH DAY TO KEEP IT HOLY.

HONOR THY FATHER AND THY MOTHER.

THOU SHALT NOT MURDER.

THOU SHALT NOT COMMIT ADULTERY.

THOU SHALT NOT STEAL.

THOU SHALT NOT BEAR FALSE WITNESS AGAINST THY NEIGHBOR.

THOU SHALT NOT COVET WHAT BELONGS TO THY NEIGHBOR."

These Commandments were given as a guide to God's people, that their lives might be happy, and acceptable to him.

In the keeping of them lay God's Covenant with his people.

The two tablets of stone were very precious. The Israelites built a golden chest to hold them, which they called the Ark. The Ark was kept in a tent-like temple, called the Tabernacle, which was carried with them wherever they went in their long journey through the desert.

The sides and curtains of the Tabernacle were covered with gold and with beautiful colored embroidery, which the Hebrews had learned to make while in Egypt.

Now that the Children of Israel had laws and a Tabernacle they appointed priests to serve them. Aaron and his sons, of the tribe of Levi, were chosen to be the first priests, for it was the Levites who helped Moses to stop the worship of the golden calf.

Aaron was the first High Priest among the Israelites, and they dressed him in an embroidered robe of blue, bordered with pomegranates of blue and purple and scarlet. There were bells of gold between the pomegranates, which tinkled when Aaron walked. On his breast were twelve precious stones, bearing the names of the twelve tribes of Israel. He wore a linen turban on his head, called a mitre, on the front of which was a band of pure gold, with the words, HOLY TO JEHOVAH.

Aaron's sons wore priestly robes also, and together they cared for the Tabernacle, and offered sacrifices for the people.

ON THE MOVE AGAIN

THE Hebrews had at last become a real nation, with laws to govern them, and judges to enforce the laws. God was their ruler, while Moses was their uncrowned king.

They had a Tabernacle and priests for the worship of God.

After camping nearly a year on the plain of Horeb, they began their slow march northward toward the Promised Land of Canaan.

The pillar of cloud that had guided them across the desert now moved above the Ark, which held the two tablets of Commandments and was carried by men from the tribe of Levi.

They often passed through regions where there was little food or water. To be sure, the manna which fell every night never failed them. But they longed for the fish and green vegetables of Egypt — for cucumbers and melons and leeks and onions and garlic. " Who will give us flesh to eat? " they cried. " We have nothing but this manna to look upon! "

Moses heard the people complaining in their tents, and he was troubled and even angry with them, that they should find so much fault.

But as usual, Moses took his trouble to God, and God said : " To-morrow the people shall have flesh to eat. They shall eat it not only one day, nor two days, nor five days, neither ten days, nor twenty days, but a whole month, until they can eat no more, and it is loathsome to them, because they have not trusted in Jehovah, but have cried, ' Why were we brought out of Egypt? ' "

Soon a strong wind came and brought quails from the sea, which fell around the camp of the Israelites to a distance of a day's journey in every direction. The people eagerly gathered the quails, and they ate so much, a plague of sickness spread through the camp, and many died.

Finally, Moses said that the time had come to make plans to enter the land of Canaan. So he sent twelve spies to explore the land, one man from each of the twelve tribes of Israel. The tribes were named for the twelve sons of Israel.

Moses gave full directions to his spies, saying: " Go up from the south into the hill country, and see what the land is like. Find out if the people who live there are strong or weak, few or many. See what kind of cities they live in, whether in camps or in strongholds, whether the land is fertile or barren, and whether there is wood on it or not. Keep up your courage, and bring back some of the fruits of the land, for it is the harvest season."

The Israelites were camping at this time in the wilderness of Zin, near Kadesh. The twelve spies explored all the land for a hundred miles north of them, as far as Hebron in the land of Canaan.

At last, the men came to a valley where grapes were growing in enormous bunches. They cut off a bunch of grapes which were so heavy two men were needed to carry it.

The spies knew that the Israelites would not believe them, if they were told about these grapes, so they started back to camp carrying the bunch with them. They also carried ripe figs and pomegranates.

THE REPORT OF THE SPIES

THERE was great excitement in the camp near Kadesh, when the twelve spies returned, bringing with them the wonderful bunch of grapes and other fruits. The men had been gone from camp forty days, and had seen many strange sights.

Caleb, who was the leader of the group, was the first to give his report to Moses and Aaron, while the people gathered in a great crowd to hear all that was said.

"We went to the land of Canaan, to which you sent us," Caleb said, "and we found it, indeed, a land full of milk and honey. See, here are some of the fruits of the land. But the people who live there are strong, and their cities are large, with high walls around them.

" The Amalekites live in the southern part of the land, while the Hittites and the Jebusites and the Amorites live in the hill country. The Canaanites live by the sea and along the river Jordan. Come, let us go up at once and take the land, for we are well able to conquer it."

Joshua agreed with Caleb that they should go immediately and seize the land of Canaan. But the ten other spies were afraid, and said : " We are not able to go up against those people, for they are stronger than we are. The men whom we saw there are of great height. The sons of Anak, who are giants, live there. We looked like grasshoppers beside them."

When the people heard the bad report of the ten spies, they were frightened, and wept all night.

They cried: "Oh, that we had died in Egypt, or here in the wilderness! Why has God brought us into this land to be killed by the sword? Our wives and our little ones will be taken from us. Would it not be better for us to go back to Egypt?"

Some of the men began talking together, and said, "Let us choose a captain from among us, and return to Egypt."

When Moses and Aaron heard this, they fell on their faces before the Children of Israel. And Caleb and Joshua said to the people: "The land which we passed through to spy out is an exceedingly good land. If God is pleased with us, he will lead us into it, and will give it to us. It is a rich land, full of milk and honey. Only do not rebel against God, nor fear the people of the land, for they will supply us with food. They have no one to defend them, but Jehovah is with us."

But the Israelites would not listen to Caleb

241

and Joshua and cried, "Stone them with stones."

God heard the distrust and rebellion of his people, and would have punished them, but Moses prayed for their forgiveness, saying: "Pardon, I pray thee, out of thy great love, the sins of this people, even as thou hast forgiven them from the time they left Egypt until now."

DISCOURAGEMENTS

AND God answered Moses: "I have heard your prayer, and will pardon the Children of Israel. But no one who saw the wonders that I worked in Egypt or in the wilderness and would not obey my voice, shall see the Promised Land. Only Caleb and Joshua, who have faithfully followed me, will I bring into the land to which they went, and their children shall possess it.

"To-morrow turn ye, and get you back

into the desert by way of the Red Sea. You and your children shall wander in the desert forty years, one year for each day that you spied out the land. Your dead bodies shall fall in the wilderness, but your children will I bring into the land that you have refused."

When Moses told these words to the Israelites, they mourned greatly. A few of them tried to go on and win their goal, but they were killed by the Amalekites and the Canaanites. The others turned their backs sadly on the Promised Land, and for nearly forty years wandered through the desert, living the life of shepherds, as Abraham and Isaac did before them.

This wandering life was not easy. Sickness often came among them and killed many of their people. Once nearly fifteen thousand died from a great plague. Moses' sister Miriam died, and the people mourned for her thirty days, as was their custom.

So the years slipped by. Nearly all of the older Israelites died, but their children grew up to be strong and brave.

At last, when they were camping again near Kadesh, Moses decided to try once more to reach the Promised Land. He did not want to go up through the South Country where the twelve spies had gone, for unfriendly tribes lived there. But east of them lived the Edomites, who were their kinsmen. So Moses sent messengers to the king of Edom, asking if the Israelites might pass through his land.

The messengers said to the king: " Your kinsmen say to you : You know that our fathers went down to Egypt to live, and that the Egyptians ill-treated them and us. We cried to Jehovah for help, and he sent a messenger, and brought us out of Egypt.

" We are now in Kadesh, on the border of your land. We pray you to let us pass through your country. We will not go through your fields or your vineyards, and will not drink water from your wells. We will follow the king's highway, and turn neither to the right nor to the left, until we have passed your border."

But the Edomites did not trust the Israelites, and their king said: "You shall not pass through our land, for we will come out with the sword against you."

The Israelites sent again to Edom, saying: "We will keep to your main highway, and if any of us, or our cattle, should drink of your water, we will pay you the price of it; only let us pass through."

Again the king said, "You shall not pass through." And he came out with great numbers of his people to keep the Israelites from entering his land.

THE END OF THE JOURNEY FOR MOSES AND AARON

THE Israelites did not want to fight the Edomites, so they turned to the south and took the longer journey around the land of Edom. They had not gone far when they came to Mount Hor, a high, barren mountain on the border of Edom. Here God spoke to Moses and Aaron. He told them to go to the top of the mountain, and take with them Aaron's son Eliezer. He then told them to put Aaron's priestly robes upon Eliezer, for Aaron must die.

When Moses and Eliezer came down the mountain without Aaron, the people wept for him thirty days. Then they started again on their long journey around Edom.

Often they did not have enough food or water. Again they became discouraged, and complained to God, crying: " Why have you brought us out of Egypt to die in this wilderness? There is no bread and no water. We loathe this manna."

Poisonous serpents soon appeared among the people. Many were bitten and died. Others came to Moses, crying: "We have sinned in speaking against God and against you. Pray that these serpents be taken away."

So Moses prayed again for his people, and God said to him: "Make a serpent of brass and set it upon a standard. If a man is bitten, let him look upon the serpent of brass, and he shall live." And many were saved.

At last the Israelites came to the land of the Amorites. Moses sent messengers to their king, as he had done to the king of Edom, saying: "Let us pass through your land. We will not turn aside into your fields or your vineyards, or drink from your wells, but will follow the king's highway until we are beyond your borders."

King Sihon feared the great multitude of

wanderers, so he gathered his people together and went out and fought against them. But the Israelites killed many of the Amorites with their swords, and took their land and their cities.

Moses was growing old, and God told him that his time had come to die. So he blessed the Israelites, calling each tribe by name, and he told them that Joshua would be their leader in his place.

Moses then said to Joshua, before all the people : " Be brave and strong, for you shall bring this people into the land promised to their fathers. God will lead you and will not forsake you."

Moses then went alone across the plains of Moab to Mount Nebo. Slowly he climbed to the top of Pisgah, which is across the river from Jericho. From the summit of this mountain he could see far into the promised country, and to the Great Sea beyond.

MOSES LOOKS UPON THE PROMISED LAND

" This is the land that I have promised to give to the children of Abraham and Isaac and Jacob," God said to him. " I have brought you here that you might see it, though you cannot go over."

So Moses died in sight of the Promised Land, when he was a hundred and twenty years old; and no one knows the place of his burial.

THE PROMISED LAND

JOSHUA AND HIS SPIES

THE forty years of wandering shepherd-life were nearly over for the Hebrew people. Joshua became their leader after Moses and Aaron had both died.

The long, hard training in the wilderness made many changes among the Israelites. When they left Egypt, they were a frightened crowd of fleeing slaves. Now they were a united nation, about to win back the land that had once belonged to their fathers.

But the river Jordan lay between them and the Promised Land. It was deep and swift at this season of the year, for the spring rains were overflowing its banks.

The red glow of the Hebrew camp fires could be seen for a long distance, against the dark sky at night. The people on the Canaan side of the Jordan became anxious, when they heard that this great army of wanderers was planning to cross the river and seize the land.

The cities of Canaan had strong walls about them, and the Canaanites had more trained soldiers than the Hebrews. But the people had heard that the God of the Hebrews was a victorious God, and they feared him.

While the Israelites were camping at Shittim, beyond the river Jordan, God spoke to Joshua, saying: "Arise, go over the Jordan, with all this people, to the land that I have promised to give to them. As I was with Moses, so I will be with you. I will not fail you nor forsake you. Only be brave and strong, and keep faithfully the law, as Moses commanded you. Turn not from it to the right nor to the left, and success shall follow you wherever you go. Fear not, nor be afraid, for Jehovah your God is with you."

Joshua was a wise general. He secretly sent out two men, saying to them, "Go, explore the land of Canaan beyond the Jordan and the walled city of Jericho."

So the two Hebrew spies swam across the flooded river and secretly entered the gates of Jericho.

The people soon noticed the two strange men in their city, and reported them to the king, saying: "Behold two men from the Children of Israel came into the city to-night to spy out the land."

The king of Jericho immediately started a search for the men, and traced them to the home of a woman named Rahab.

Rahab hid the men under a heap of flax that was drying on the roof of her house. But she let the searchers think that she had seen the two spies leave the city through the great gate, just before dark. And she said: "Follow after them quickly, for you may overtake them."

So the men of Jericho went to search for the two Hebrews beyond the city walls, and the heavy gates were closed behind them for the night.

THE ESCAPE OF THE SPIES

AFTER she had sent the pursuers away, Rahab hurried to the roof of her house and talked with the two Hebrews.

" I know that Jehovah has given our land to you," she said, " and the fear of you has fallen upon us all. We have heard how Jehovah dried up the waters of the Red Sea before you, when you came out of Egypt, and how you utterly destroyed the Amorites beyond the Jordan. There is no courage left in any of our men because of you, for Jehovah, your God, is God in heaven above and in the earth beneath.

" I pray you to promise, as I have shown kindness to you to-day, that you will show kindness to my father and mother, and to my brothers and sisters, and will save their lives when you come to take our city."

"Your lives for our lives," said the two men. "If you will tell no one what our business here is, we will treat you kindly and honestly when God gives us the land."

Rahab then let the men down from her window by a cord, for her house was built against the side of the city wall.

"Flee to the mountains!" she said to them, "or the pursuers will find you. Hide yourselves there for three days, until they have returned. Then go on your way."

"We cannot keep our promise to save you and your family," said the two men, "unless you tie to your window this scarlet cord, by which you have let us down. We shall then know which is your house when we return to take the city.

"Bring your father and your mother and all your family into the house. If any one

257

should leave it and should go into the street, we cannot be blamed for his death. But if you keep our secret, those who are in this house shall be saved."

" I will do as you say," Rahab answered. And when they were gone, she tied the scarlet cord to her window.

The two Hebrews hurried through the dark to the hills, where they hid for three days. Their pursuers hunted for them in every direction, but did not find them, and so returned to the city.

The two men then came out of their hiding place and crossed the river Jordan and reported to Joshua all that had happened to them, saying, " Truly, God has given the land into our hands, for the people are afraid, and melt away before us."

So Joshua rose early the next morning and moved their camp from Shittim to the banks of the Jordan, where they made ready to pass over.

Joshua then said to the people, " Put all evil out of your hearts, for to-morrow Jehovah will do wonders among you. So shall you know that a living God is with you."

As they stood by the banks of the overflowing river, Joshua said to the priests, " Take up the Ark of the Lord and pass over ahead of the people."

CROSSING THE JORDAN

In dry weather it was an easy matter to cross the river Jordan, although there were no bridges. Very little water came down from the hills, except in the rainy season, and there were many shallow places in the river where people could wade across.

But in the spring of the year the river was deep and wide, often overflowing its lower banks. At such times one could cross only by swimming.

This was the condition of the Jordan when Joshua said to the priests, " Take up the Ark of the Lord and pass over ahead of the people."

Great faith and courage were needed to obey this command, but God had promised that he would not fail them. So the priests took up the precious Ark, which held the two tablets of Commandments, and moved toward the river, while the great multitude of people prepared to follow, with their cattle and tents and all their household goods.

As the priests came near the Jordan, their feet dipped into the edge of the water, and a wonderful thing began to happen. Far up the river the water seemed to stop flowing, or in some strange way it was held back. Soon no water was flowing between the Israelites and the land of Canaan, and the people and all their cattle passed over on the soft ground of the river bed. The priests, carrying the Ark on their shoulders, stood in the middle of the river bed, while the long procession passed by.

When they had all reached the other side, Joshua called twelve men to him, one from each of the twelve tribes of Israel, and said to them, " Go again to the place where the Ark stood in the middle of the river. Let each man there take a stone and put it upon his shoulder and bring it to the place where we shall camp to-night. The stones shall be piled one upon another and shall be a reminder to us. In the years to come, when your children ask, ' What do these stones mean?' You shall say to them, ' They are a reminder that the water in the river was held back before the Ark of Jehovah, when it passed over the Jordan.' "

The men did as Joshua commanded. They took from the middle of the Jordan twelve stones, one for each of the twelve tribes of Israel, and they carried them to Gilgal, where the Israelites were to camp that night. The water of the river then returned and overflowed its banks once more.

The Children of Israel were at last in the land of their fathers. One of the first things that they did was to celebrate the feast of the Passover, in memory of the night when the Angel of Death passed over their homes in Egypt, and when they started on their long journey toward freedom.

They had now no more need of the manna that had not failed them for forty years. They had reached the Promised Land, which was " flowing with milk and honey."

THE FALL OF JERICHO

THE land of Canaan was like a paradise to the Children of Israel who had lived for so many years in the bare, dry desert. It was a rich, fertile country, with trees and fruits and fields of ripening grain.

But the people who lived in the land worshiped idols of wood and stone, and they lived selfish, sinful lives. During their years in the wilderness, the Hebrews had learned to trust in the one living God, who required clean, unselfish lives of his followers. This meant a long, hard struggle between the forces of good and of evil.

On arriving in the Promised Land, the Israelites set up their tents around their Tabernacle, on the heights of Gilgal above the Jordan. This was to be their headquarters for several years.

The rich and wicked city of Jericho was only three miles away. The Israelites knew that they must take this city before they could go any farther into the land of Canaan. But the people of Jericho had closed their gates since the visit of the two spies, and no one was allowed to go in or out.

But Joshua prayed for help, and God said to him, " I will give Jericho to you, with its king and all its strong warriors. Only do as I say."

So Joshua called all the people together, and gave them God's commands. He said : " Seven priests shall march around the city of Jericho, blowing upon seven trumpets of rams' horns. Other priests shall follow, carrying the Ark of the Lord upon their shoulders. Armed men shall go before the priests, and other armed men shall follow those who bear the Ark. You shall march around the city with trumpets blowing, but no man shall shout or even speak, until I tell you to do so."

So the priests carrying the trumpets, and those carrying the Ark of the Lord, with forty thousand armed men, marched around the walls of Jericho, after which they returned to camp and rested for the night. The next day they rose early and marched again around Jericho, with trumpets blowing.

For six days they did this, but on the

JOSHUA BEFORE JERICHO

seventh day they rose with the dawn and marched seven times around the city. On the seventh time, while the priests were blowing their trumpets, Joshua cried: "Shout! For Jehovah has given you the city. Only Rahab and her family shall be saved, for it was she who hid our messengers. Take nothing from the city except silver and gold, and vessels of brass and iron. These shall be purified and put into the treasury of Jehovah. All else is accursed, because of the wickedness of the people. Shout!"

The thousands of armed men then gave their battle cry. The priests blew upon their trumpets, and all the Israelites joined in the great shout.

The walls of Jericho shook, and fell to the ground, and the army of Israelites rushed in and took the city.

THE DEFEAT AT AI

WHEN he saw that the walls of Jericho had fallen, Joshua said to the two spies, " Go now to Rahab's house, as you have promised her, and bring the woman out of the city, with all that she has."

So the young men brought out Rahab and her family, and all that belonged to her. And the city of Jericho was burned to the ground. Only the silver and gold, and the vessels of brass and iron were saved and put into the treasury of the Lord.

Joshua then sent men to spy out the small city of Ai, about ten miles away in the hills.

The spies returned and said to Joshua: " There are only a few men in the city. Two or three thousand of our men can easily capture it. Do not send up all your soldiers."

So Joshua sent three thousand men up the narrow, rocky pass to take the little town of Ai, which was built on the top of a hill, three thousand feet above the camp at Gilgal.

But something was wrong with the Israelite soldiers. They turned and fled as soon as the men of Ai came out to attack them, and thirty-six Israelites were killed.

This defeat filled the hearts of the Israelites with fear.

Joshua and the elders of Israel rent their clothes, and put dust upon their heads, and fell down on their faces before the Ark of Jehovah until evening.

Joshua cried: "Alas, O Lord, why have you brought these people over Jordan to perish! What can I say, when the Israelites have turned their backs before their enemies? The people of the land will hear of it, and they will surround us and wipe us off the earth. What wilt thou do, O Lord, for thy great name?"

And Jehovah said to Joshua: "Get thee up. Why hast thou fallen on thy face?

Israel has sinned. They have disobeyed my command. They have stolen and have deceived, therefore the Children of Israel cannot stand before their enemies. Up, purify the people and yourselves before to-morrow, for this sin must be taken away from among you."

Early on the morrow, Joshua called all the tribes of Israel before him and found that the sin was in the tribe of Judah. This tribe then passed before Joshua, family by family, and man by man, until Achan appeared.

And Joshua said to Achan: "My son, make confession before the God of Israel. Tell me now what you have done. Hide it not from me."

And Achan answered: "Truly I have sinned against Jehovah. When I saw among the ruins of Jericho a beautiful Babylonian mantle and two hundred shekels of silver, and a wedge of gold weighing fifty shekels,

I coveted them exceedingly and took them."

So Joshua sent messengers, who ran to Achan's tent and brought the stolen goods.

Then Joshua, and all Israel, took Achan and his family, with their stolen mantle and the silver and gold, and they stoned them with stones.

And the place is called the valley of Achor, unto this day.

THE VICTORY AT AI

After Achan's sin was punished, God said to Joshua: "Fear not. Arise, take your men of war and go up to Ai, for I will give the city into your hand. You shall do to Ai and her king what you did to Jericho and her king. And you shall take what you want of the spoils and the cattle."

So Joshua sent thirty thousand of his soldiers that night to hide in the deep ravines west of Ai.

Joshua said to his men: "You shall lie in hiding behind the city, and watch for my command. To-morrow I will take other soldiers, and go up as if to attack the city. But when the men of Ai come out against us, as they did before, we will turn and flee from them. Then they, and all their people, will follow after us, leaving the city unguarded and the gates wide open. I will then give you a signal to come up from your hiding-places and take the city."

So Joshua sent his soldiers forth, and they lay in ambush all night.

Early the next morning, Joshua took five thousand other soldiers and with the elders of Israel they marched against Ai.

When the king of Ai saw the small band of Israelites coming, he gathered his men and went out to meet them, remembering how easily he had defeated them before. But he did not know of the thirty thousand soldiers lying in hiding behind his city.

This was just what Joshua had expected. Instead of going up at once to fight and take the city, Joshua's men now turned as if they were retreating, with the king of Ai and all his people hard after them. There was not a man left either in Ai or in Bethel, for all were in pursuit of the Israelites. And the gates of the cities were left wide open.

Joshua then raised his javelin and signaled to the army in ambush, and the soldiers ran quickly up into the city and set it on fire.

When the king of Ai and his men looked behind them and saw smoke rising above their city, they did not know which way to turn. Their city was burning, and they were surrounded by thousands of Israelites, both before them and behind them.

Joshua and his men then turned and smote the people from Ai with their bows and arrows, and with their swords. Not one escaped.

That night twelve thousand men had fallen. Ai and all her people were completely destroyed. Before the city was burned, the Israelites took away the cattle and many other things.

The city of Bethel was taken also, and many people fled in great fear from other villages near by.

The Children of Israel were slowly but surely winning their way into the Promised Land.

DAYS OF PEACE

Soon after the victory of Ai, the Israelites took a long journey into the central part of Canaan to the beautiful little valley between Mount Ebal and Mount Gerizim.

Here, long years before, Abraham and Jacob pitched their tents. And here, too, Jacob dug his well and later bought a field. Here the Israelites now buried the body of

Joseph, which they had brought with them from Egypt.

On the top of Mount Ebal, Joshua built a stone altar where the people offered burnt offerings to Jehovah. And they held a great service, half of the people standing on the slopes of Mount Ebal and half on Mount Gerizim, while Joshua and the priests, with the altar of the Lord, stood in the narrow valley between.

Joshua read aloud, so that all might hear, the laws that Moses gave to his people, for only by obeying these laws could the Israelites expect God's blessing.

When the service was over, the Israelites returned to their camping place at Gilgal.

All of Canaan had now heard of the strange people whose God had held back the water in the Red Sea and in the river Jordan, so that they might pass over on dry ground. They had heard, also, of the capture of Jericho and of Ai, and they were afraid.

But the people of Gibeon thought of a clever way to save their cities, and to escape being killed.

Some of their men dressed themselves in ragged clothes and muddy shoes. They put hard, mouldy bread into old sacks on their donkeys, and took wine skins that were torn and mended.

These men then went to Gilgal to talk with the Israelites. They looked as if they had traveled many weeks.

"We have come from a far country," they said to Joshua, "and we want to make peace with you. We have heard of Jehovah your God, and all that he did in Egypt, and of how he led you through the wilderness into this land. Come, let us be friends. Promise that you will not kill us or destroy our cities."

But Joshua said to them: "Who are you? How can we know that you do not live in this land?"

"See this bread," they answered him. "We took it hot from the oven the day we started, and now it is dry and mouldy. These wine skins, too, were new when we filled them, and our clothes and shoes have grown old from the long journey."

The Israelites believed the men, and without asking wisdom from God, they promised that the lives of the Gibeonites should be safe, and their cities should not be harmed or destroyed.

But three days later the Israelites heard that these same Gibeonites were their neighbors, living in four cities near by.

At first, the Israelites were angry and wanted to break their promise. But Joshua said: "We have given our word and must keep it. Let the people live, but because they have deceived us, they shall be our servants. They shall cut our wood, and draw our water, and carry our burdens." And so they did ever after.

THE BATTLE OF THE FIVE KINGS

THE days of fighting were not over for the Children of Israel. When the king of Jerusalem heard that the Gibeonites had made peace with Israel, he sent to the kings of four other cities near Jerusalem, saying, " Come up and help me, and together we will destroy the Gibeonites, for they have made peace with our enemies, and are serving them."

So the five kings gathered their men together and went up with a great army to attack Gibeon.

But the people of Gibeon sent in haste to Joshua, saying, " Come quickly and save us, for the kings of the Amorites, who live in the hill country, have gathered together against us."

So Joshua and his men started at once to help the Gibeonites. They marched all night up a steep, rough trail, for Gibeon,

276

like many other cities in Canaan, was built on a high hill, where the people could easily defend themselves.

In the early morning, Joshua and his men came suddenly upon the army of the five kings camping near the city.

The Amorites were so surprised and alarmed at seeing the Israelite army, they turned and fled down the narrow pass, up which they had so recently come. And the men of Israel raced after them.

There was a great battle in the pass of Beth-horon that day. In the midst of it a terrible hailstorm came, which killed more of the fleeing soldiers than the swords of the Israelites had done.

The five kings escaped and hid themselves in a mountain cave, but they were later found and put to death.

Other kings in the north banded together, also, to stand against Joshua, but he overcame them all. After a few more small battles, the war between Canaan and Israel was ended. There were a number of cities that had not yet been taken, but the Israelites were tired of war. They already held so much of the country that Joshua decided to divide the land between the twelve tribes and let them settle down.

Joshua said to the people: "God has given you a land for which you have not labored, and vineyards and olive groves which you did not plant, and cities which you did not build. Now put away from among you all strange idols, such as the Canaanites serve, and serve always the God of your fathers."

And the people answered: "We will never turn away from the God who brought us out of Egypt into this land. He is the God of Israel. We will serve him forever."

Joshua wrote down their promise in the Book of the Law, where others might read it. He set up a great stone under an oak

278

tree in Shechem, saying, "This stone shall stand as a witness of your promise to be faithful to Jehovah your God."

Joshua then sent the people away, each tribe to his own land. And the country was no longer called Canaan, but the land of Israel.

A few years later Joshua died, being a hundred and ten years old.

THE ISRAELITES WORSHIP IDOLS

As long as the Israelites lived who had known Moses and Joshua, they did not forget the God who had led them into the Promised Land. But when their children and grandchildren grew up, they began to worship idols of the earth-god Baal, and to do sinful things, as the people around them did. They were no longer strong and brave, as their fathers were, for they seldom asked for God's help.

Little by little, the lands of the Israelites

were overrun by strange neighbors, and their herds were driven away. But some of them remembered how God had helped their fathers in earlier days, and they called upon him for help again.

Each time that they left their idols and turned to God, he brought them out of their trouble. But every time they forgot him again, after a few years, and went back to their idols and their sinful lives.

Finally, some Arabs living in the land of Midian began to cross the river Jordan each year, just at the harvest time, and to carry away the crops of grain which the Hebrews had grown.

These Midianites brought their tents and their families with them. They came so quickly and in such great numbers, they were like swarms of locusts. Their herds and camels ate up all the grass in the fields, leaving the poor Israelites but little food for their own cattle.

At last the people of Israel did not even
dare to stay in their own villages, but hid
themselves in caves in the mountains. If
anyone succeeded in raising a little grain,
he hid it in a pit and covered it with earth,
or put it in an empty wine press, where the
Midianites could not find it.

This went on for seven long years before
the Israelites thought to ask God for his help.

One day a man named Gideon was threshing out wheat when an angel of God appeared
to him.

The angel said to Gideon, " Jehovah is
with you."

And Gideon answered : " If Jehovah is
with us, why then has all this happened to
us? Our fathers have told us of the wonderful things that God did when he brought
us out of Egypt. But now he has cast us
off and has delivered us to the Midianites."

The angel looked upon Gideon, and said :
" You are a strong man. Go, save Israel

from the hand of Midian. It is God who sends you."

"How can I save Israel, my Lord?" Gideon cried. "My family is the poorest in Manasseh, and I am the youngest in my father's house."

But the angel of God said: "Surely God will be with you. You shall drive out the Midianites as if they were one man. But you must first free your own people from the worship of false gods."

GIDEON TEARS DOWN THE ALTAR TO BAAL

GIDEON'S own father, Joash, had built an altar to Baal, with a large wooden idol, on a high lookout near his house, for, like many other Israelites, Joash had forsaken the God of his fathers.

God had said that Gideon must free the Israelites from the worship of idols before he could drive the Midianites out of the country.

AN ANGEL SITTING UNDER AN OAK
APPEARS TO GIDEON

So that night, when no one could see them, Gideon and ten of his father's servants tore down the altar to Baal and broke into pieces the wooden idol.

On the same spot, Gideon built an altar to the God of Israel. He then placed the broken pieces of the wooden idol on this altar and offered a young ox for a burnt offering.

The next morning, when the people of the village came out to worship their idols, they found them gone and their altar torn down. In its place stood an altar to the living God, with the broken idol burning under a sacrifice to the Lord.

"Who has done this thing?" the people cried to each other.

"Gideon, the son of Joash, did it in the night," someone said.

Then they all ran to the house of Joash, crying: "Bring him out that we may stone him, for he has torn down the altar to Baal and the image."

" Cannot Baal take care of himself? " Gideon's father said to the people. " If he is a god, let him punish the man who has destroyed his altar. Does Baal need you to save him? "

But Baal could not harm the man who had broken the images. When the people saw this, they forsook their idols and turned again to Jehovah their God.

Gideon now sent messengers to all the people in his own tribe of Manasseh, and to the other tribes in that part of the land, saying: " Come, and we will drive the Midianites out of our land." He then sounded his war trumpet, and thousands of men gathered around him ready to follow his lead.

Gideon began to be afraid that he could not carry through this great thing. He prayed to God, saying: " If you would really save Israel through my hand, give me a sign. I will place a bit of wool fleece here on the threshing floor. To-morrow morning if there is dew on the fleece, while the ground around it is dry, I shall know that Israel shall be saved through me."

The next morning Gideon was out early to examine the fleece. He took it up and pressed it between his hands, and a bowlful of water came out, though the ground was dry.

But Gideon was still fearful and said: " O Lord, do not be angry with me. Let me ask for one more sign that you have chosen me. Let the fleece remain dry, while the ground around it is wet with dew." And when Gideon found it so the next morning, he was sure that God had chosen him to save Israel, and his heart grew brave.

CHOOSING HIS ARMY

GIDEON and the thirty-two thousand men who had joined him rose early the next morning, and camped by the spring of Harod on a hill above the camp of Midian.

But God said to Gideon: " Your army is too large. If you should win the victory against the Midianites, your people would say that they won it by their own might. Let those who are afraid to fight go home."

And twenty-two thousand men went home, for they were not trained to fight, and but few of them had swords or spears. Ten thousand, however, stayed bravely with Gideon.

Again God said to Gideon: " Your army is still too large. Take them down to drink at the spring of Harod, and I will show you which men to choose."

So the ten thousand men marched down the hill, as if to attack the great army of

287

Midianites camping on the plain beyond. As they came to the spring, Gideon told them to drink in haste, and he watched them as they did so.

Three hundred of the men quickly dipped up a handful of the sparkling water and drank it as they marched on. The others fell down on their knees, with their faces to the water, drinking deeply and forgetting that they were soldiers marching to battle.

God said, " With the three hundred will I save Israel, and will deliver the Midianites into your hand."

So all those who had kneeled down to drink of the water were sent back to the camp, for they would not make the best soldiers.

God then said to Gideon: " If you fear to attack the Midianites with this small army, take your servant and go down secretly into their camp and hear what they shall say. It will give you courage."

So Gideon and his servant went down to the borders of the Midianite camp and walked about as if they belonged there. What they saw was enough to fill their hearts with fear instead of with courage. Thousands of wandering Arabs covered the valley like a great swarm of locusts. Their camels were as the sand on the seashore in number. They could not be counted.

Gideon saw two men talking earnestly together, and he listened to what they were saying. One man was telling the other of a dream that he had had. He said: " I dreamed that a loaf of barley bread came falling down into our camp. It struck the tent of our chief and turned it upside down, and the tent lay flat on the ground."

The other man said: " Surely that means that Gideon the Israelite is coming down upon us with his sword. God will deliver us all into his hands."

When Gideon heard the dream and the

meaning that was given to it, he praised God in his heart and returned to the camp of Israel. He cried to his three hundred men, "Arise, for God will deliver the host of Midian into our hands."

GIDEON'S BRAVE BAND

GIDEON divided his band into three companies of one hundred men each. To each man he gave a ram's-horn trumpet, an empty pitcher, and a lighted torch. He told the men to hold the torches inside of the pitchers, so that the lights could not be seen.

Gideon then said to the men: "Keep your eyes upon me and do whatever I do. When I blow upon my trumpet, blow upon yours and shout, 'The sword of Jehovah and of Gideon!'"

In the middle of the night, Gideon and his little band marched quietly down the hill, with their lighted torches hidden inside their pitchers. The three companies were placed at some distance from each other around the camp of Midian.

Suddenly there came a loud blowing of trumpets. The pitchers were broken with a crash, and three hundred flaming torches flashed upon the sleeping Arabs, with the cry, " The sword of Jehovah and of Gideon!"

The Midianites were filled with terror. They thought only of escape. In frightful confusion they fled down a steep, narrow pass toward a ford of the Jordan, where they might cross to their own side of the river.

But they could not escape from Gideon. He sent messengers to the thousands of men who had answered his first call, and told them to go quickly in pursuit of the fleeing Arabs.

Men, women, and children, cattle and camels, tumbled over each other in their haste to get away. At every ford of the Jordan they were met by large numbers of

Israelites. Very few escaped across the river and these were followed by Gideon and his bravest men. Many thousands met death that day.

The people of Midian never left their homes to trouble Israel again.

The grateful Israelites wanted to make Gideon their king at once, and his son, and his son's son after him, for saving them from the terror of Midian.

But Gideon said: "Neither I nor my sons shall rule over you. God only shall be your ruler."

THE YOUNG SAMSON

THE years went by, and the Children of Israel did many things that were wrong in God's sight. They had much trouble with their neighbors, especially with the Philistines, who were a quarrelsome people living along the shore of the Great Sea.

These Philistines worshiped an idol called Dagon, which had the head of a fish and the body of a man.

The Philistines often sent their armies up into the hill country where the Israelites lived, and robbed them of their crops. They took away from the Israelites, too, their swords and spears, so that they could not defend themselves.

Finally, in their great trouble, the Israelites called upon God for help, and God heard their prayer.

In the tribe of Dan, whose land lay next to that of the Philistines, lived a man and woman who had no children. One day an angel came to the wife and said: "You shall have a son, and he shall help to save Israel from the Philistines. But your son must not touch wine or strong drink, as long as he lives. His hair must never be cut, and he shall make a vow to God, as the Nazarites do."

The child was named Samson, "the Destroyer." When Samson became a young man, the Philistines were still troubling the Israelites, stealing their crops and their cattle, and sometimes carrying away their women and children.

As Samson's home was close to the land of the Philistines, he often went down into their towns. One day he went down to the city of Timnah, and saw there a young woman whom he wanted to marry. He hurried back to his home and said to his father and mother, "Among the daughters of the Philistines, I have seen the woman whom I want for my wife. Go and get her for me."

His parents were troubled, and said to him: "Why do you go among the Philistines for a wife? Is there no woman among your own people for you to marry?"

But Samson only said, "Get her for me, for she pleases me."

His parents could not know that this was God's will, but they went down with their son to Timnah.

As Samson passed by the vineyards of Timnah, a young lion came roaring toward him. The man seized the lion and killed it with his hands, as easily as he would have killed a kid in his father's flock. But he did not tell his father and mother what he had done.

They went on to Timnah and talked with the Philistine woman, and again she pleased Samson well.

After a time, Samson made another trip to Timnah to take the woman for his wife. When he came near the vineyards, he stopped to look at the dead lion, and found that a swarm of bees was storing honey in its dead body.

Samson filled his hands with the honey and ate it, as he walked on, sharing it with his father and mother who were with him.

But he did not tell them where he had found the honey.

SAMSON'S RIDDLE

THE wedding feast of Samson lasted a whole week. Thirty of his young men friends attended it. One day, when they were all guessing riddles, Samson said : " If you can guess my riddle before the seventh day of the feast, I will give you thirty sheets and thirty changes of garments. But if you cannot guess it, you must give the thirty sheets and thirty garments to me."

" Let us hear your riddle," the young men cried.

And Samson said : —

"Out of the eater came something to eat,
And out of the strong came something sweet."

The men puzzled over this riddle for several days, but no one could guess it. Then they went to Samson's young wife, and said :

"Find out for us the answer to your husband's riddle, or we shall burn your father's house, and all his family in it. Were we invited here to be made poor?"

Samson's wife went weeping to her husband, crying: "Now I know that you do not love me, for you have given my people a riddle and have not told it to me."

"I have not told it to my father or my mother," Samson answered her. "Why should I tell it to you?"

But his wife still wept, and on the last day of the feast, Samson told her the riddle, because she had begged so hard for it. She then went quickly to the men and told them the answer that he had given her.

So on the seventh day of the feast, the thirty young men went to Samson and said: "Here is the answer to your riddle: What is sweeter than honey? And what is stronger than a lion?"

And Samson said to them: "If you had

not bribed my wife, you would not have guessed my riddle."

Samson was very angry, and he went out and killed thirty Philistines and gave their clothing to the thirty men. He then went home to his father's house, leaving his wife behind.

After a time, Samson's heart softened, and he took a young kid for a gift and went down to visit his wife. But her father would not allow him to see her.

" I thought you had left her," he said. " So I gave her to one of your friends. See, her sister is even fairer than she. I beg you to take her instead."

But Samson would not marry the younger sister. He was angry, and he meant to do something to punish the Philistines for cheating him a second time.

He went out and caught three hundred foxes and tied them together in pairs by their tails, with a firebrand fastened between them. When the firebrands were lighted, Samson turned the foxes loose into the ripe grain fields belonging to the Philistines.

The foxes ran wildly through the fields, setting the grain on fire as they ran, until all the grain and many olive trees were burned to the ground.

When the Philistines saw what had happened, they cried, " Who has done this thing? "

" Samson did it, because his wife was taken from him and given to his friend," someone cried.

So the people blamed Samson's wife and her father, and burned their house, with them in it.

WILD WAYS

SAMSON was grieved by the death of his young wife, and was angry over the way the Philistines had treated him, so he went out and fought them fiercely, killing many. He then hurried back to his hill country, where he hid himself in a cave of a cliff called Etam.

Soon the Philistines came up in great numbers and spread out over the land of Judah.

The people cried, "Why have you come up to trouble us?"

"We have come to find Samson and to bind him, and do to him as he has done to us," they answered.

Three thousand of the men of Judah then went down to the cave where Samson was hiding, and said to him: "Do you know what you have done to us by your wild ways? We are going to bind you and give you over to the Philistines."

"I have only done to them as they have done to me," Samson said. "But if you will promise not to kill me yourselves, you may bind me and hand me over to the Philistines."

SAMSON SLAYS THE PHILISTINES WITH THE
JAWBONE OF AN ASS

So the men of Judah bound Samson with two new ropes, and they brought him up from the cave. The Philistines shouted when they saw him, and were about to take him away, when Samson stretched his strong arms and broke the new ropes, as if they were burnt strands of flax.

The next moment Samson seized the jawbone of an ass that lay on the ground, and with his heavy blows killed a thousand of the Philistines, shouting: "With the jawbone of an ass, I pile them heaps upon heaps! With the jawbone of an ass, I have killed a thousand men!"

One evening, not long after this, Samson went down into the land of the Philistines again, for he was not afraid of them. He went to their chief city, Gaza, which was surrounded by a high wall.

When the people saw that Samson had gone into the city, they closed and locked the great gate behind him, and told each other that when he came out in the morning, they would take him and kill him.

Samson must have heard of their plan, for about midnight he rose and went quietly to the gate, as if to go home. The gate was locked and barred, but Samson put his great strength against it. He lifted the two heavy doors, posts, bar, and all, and put them upon his shoulders and walked away. If any of the Philistines saw him, they were too frightened by his great strength to say anything.

Samson carried the gate of Gaza for twenty miles over into his own land. He took it to the top of a high hill, and left it near the city of Hebron.

By such deeds as these, Samson kept the Philistines in constant fear of him, and they did not dare to ill-treat the Israelites, as they had done earlier.

DELILAH AND SAMSON

AFTER a number of years Samson loved Delilah, another Philistine woman.

The rulers of the Philistines now thought that through Delilah they could easily get Samson into their power. They said to her: "We will each give you eleven hundred pieces of silver, if you will find out for us what it is that gives Samson his great strength. Tell us how we can overcome him and bind him, so that we can punish him."

The offer of so much money was too great a temptation for Delilah. She said to Samson: "I beg you to tell me what gives you your great strength. How could one bind you strongly enough to punish you?"

Samson knew that the Philistines wanted to take him, and he said to Delilah: "If I were bound with seven green bowstrings that had not been dried, I should become as weak as any other man."

Delilah told the rulers of the Philistines what Samson had said, and they brought her seven green bowstrings, with which she bound Samson while he was sleeping.

Delilah hid the Philistines in an inner room until Samson was tightly bound, then she wakened him by crying, " The Philistines are upon you, Samson ! "

Samson woke with a start, and the strings with which he was bound broke as easily as yarn would have done, if it had been burned by a fire.

Delilah then said to Samson : " You have made fun of me, and have told me lies. Now tell me truly how you could be bound."

" Bind me with new ropes that have never been used," Samson said, " and I shall become weak like other men."

So, when he was sleeping soundly, Delilah took new ropes and bound him again, and cried, " The Philistines are upon you, Samson ! "

The men who were watching from the inner room saw Samson break the ropes from his arms, as if they had been threads, and no one dared to touch him.

But Delilah did not give up hope. She thought of the money that had been promised her, and again she said to Samson: "You are only deceiving me and making fun of me. Now tell me, I beg of you, how you could be tightly bound?"

"If you should weave the seven braids of my long hair into the web of your loom, and fasten it with the weaving pin, I should then be no stronger than any other man," Samson said to her.

So, one day, when Samson fell asleep near her loom, Delilah caught his long braids and wove them into the web, fastening them with the weaving pin. And she cried again, "The Philistines are upon you, Samson!"

But when Samson woke from his sleep, he rose, easily lifting the beam, and the web, and the pin that was fastened to his hair, for he was as strong as ever.

THE SECRET OF SAMSON'S STRENGTH

DAY after day Delilah urged Samson to tell her the secret of his strength.

"How can you say that you love me," she said, "when you will not trust me with your secret? Three times you have deceived me, and would not tell me how you get your great strength."

Samson became tired with her constant urging, and finally told her the whole story of his strength.

"No razor has ever touched my head," he said, "for I am under a vow to God. If my hair were cut, my strength would go from me, and I should become like any other man."

Delilah knew that at last he had told her the truth. She sent quickly for the

306

Philistine rulers, saying, "Come up once more, for Samson has told me all that is in his heart."

The rulers came, each bringing eleven hundred pieces of silver with him.

Delilah made her husband go to sleep with his head upon her lap, and she called for a man to come and shave off the seven braids from his head. Then she began to mock him, and to say, "The Philistines are upon you, Samson!"

"This is only another trick," Samson thought, as he woke, "I will go out and shake myself free." But his strength had gone from him, because he had broken his vow to God.

The jealous Philistines quickly seized him and put out both his eyes, so that he might never harm them again. They put chains of brass upon him and took him down to the prison in Gaza, where he was made to turn the heavy millstones that ground the grain.

But while Samson was in prison, he re-newed his vow to God. His hair grew again, and his strength returned.

The Philistines thought that it was Dagon, their fish-god, who had given Samson into their hands. So they held a great feast in the temple of Dagon, and Samson was brought from the prison to make sport for them.

The temple was filled with men and women, and three thousand people were gathered on the roof to see the sport.

Samson came slowly into the temple, led by a small boy, for he was blind.

" Lead me to the pillars which hold up the temple," Samson said to the lad, " for I would lean against them."

As Samson stood between two of the pillars, he prayed to the God of Israel : " O Lord God, remember me, I pray thee, and strengthen me only this once, that I may punish the Philistines for taking my eyes."

Then Samson took hold of the two middle pillars, upon which the temple rested, and leaned against them, saying, " Let me die with the Philistines."

With all his might Samson bowed forward. The pillars crumbled and the roof fell, crushing all the people that were in the temple. He had killed more on the day of his death than he had during his whole life.

When Samson's father and brothers heard what had happened, they came down and carried his body back to the family burial place.

Samson had been a Judge in Israel for twenty years.